Author's Purpose

Cause and Effect

Classify and Categorize

Compare and Contrast

Details and Facts

Draw Conclusions

Graphic Sources

Literary Elements

Main Idea and Details

Sequence

Steps in a Process

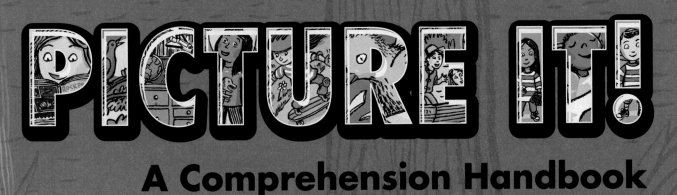

PICTURE IT!

A Comprehension Handbook

Author's Purpose

Authors write to inform or entertain.

To Inform

To Entertain

Cause and Effect

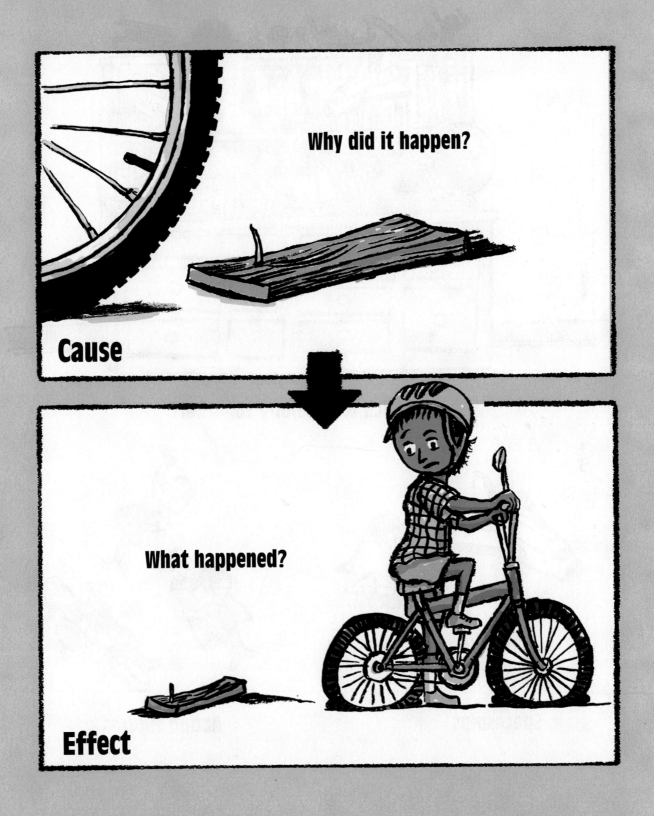

Why did it happen?

Cause

What happened?

Effect

Classify and Categorize

Which toys belong together?

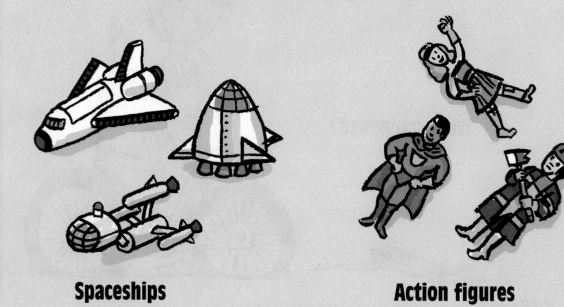

Spaceships

Action figures

Compare and Contrast

How are
we alike?

How are
we different?

Details and Facts

Draw Conclusions

Use what you already know to help you understand what is happening.

Graphic Sources

Time Line

How I Get Ready for School

6:30 7:00 7:30 8:00 8:30 9:00

Circle Graph

How We All Get There

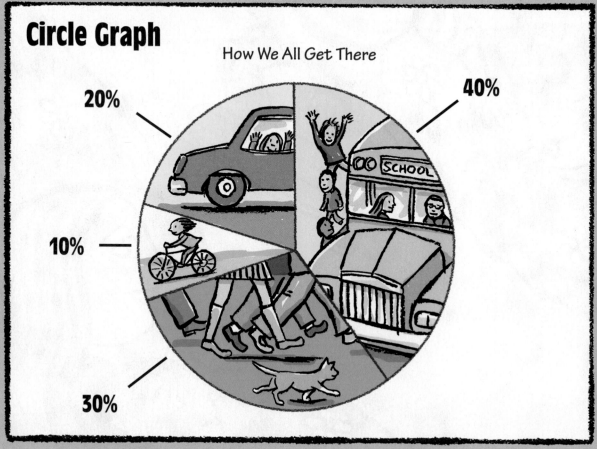

20% 40% 10% 30%

Main Idea and Details

Main Idea

What is the selection all about?

Details

Sequence

What happens first, next, and last?

Steps in a Process

Literary Elements

Characters

Plot

Beginning **Middle** **End**

What happens in the beginning, middle, and end of the story?

Problem/Solution

Problem

Solution

Setting

Where and when does the story take place?

Theme

What is the big idea in the story?

Acknowledgments appear on pages 218–219, which constitute an extension of this copyright page.

ISBN-13:   978-0-328-63435-4
ISBN-10:   0-328-63435-2
9 10 V011 14

PEARSON LANGUAGE CENTRAL

ELD

Consulting Authors

Jim Cummins, Ph.D.

Lily Wong Fillmore, Ph.D.

Georgia García, Ph.D.

Jill Kerper Mora, Ed.D.

PEARSON

Glenview, Illinois • Boston, Massachusetts • Chandler, Arizona • Upper Saddle River, New Jersey

Get Online!

Picture It! A Comprehension Handbook PI•1–PI•13
Words! A Vocabulary Handbook W•1–W•14

Unit 1 Exploration

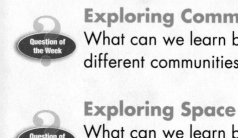

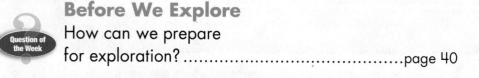

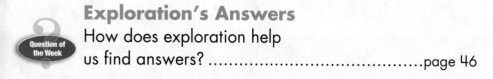
Unit 2 Working Together

Unit 3 Creative Ideas

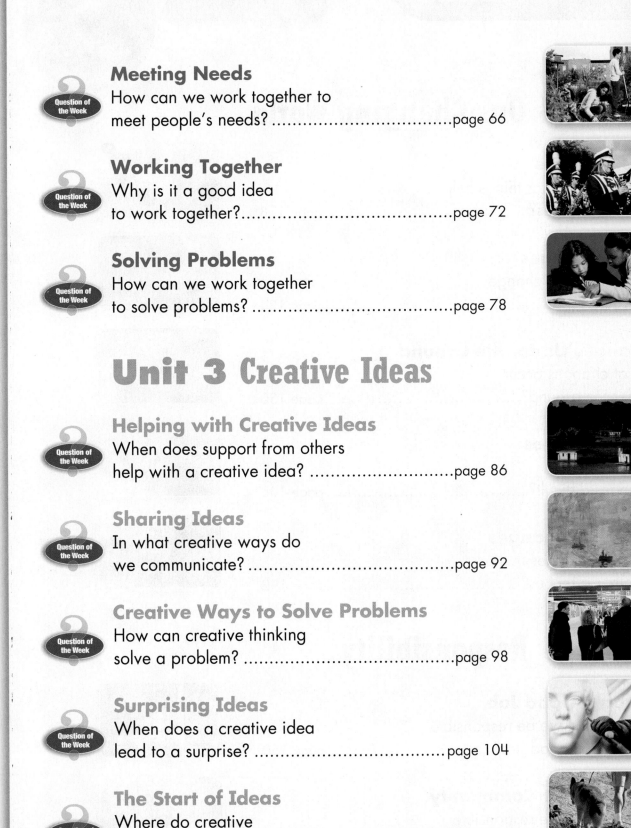

Get
Online!

Unit 4 Our Changing World

Unit 5 Responsibility

Question of
the Week

Unit 6 Traditions

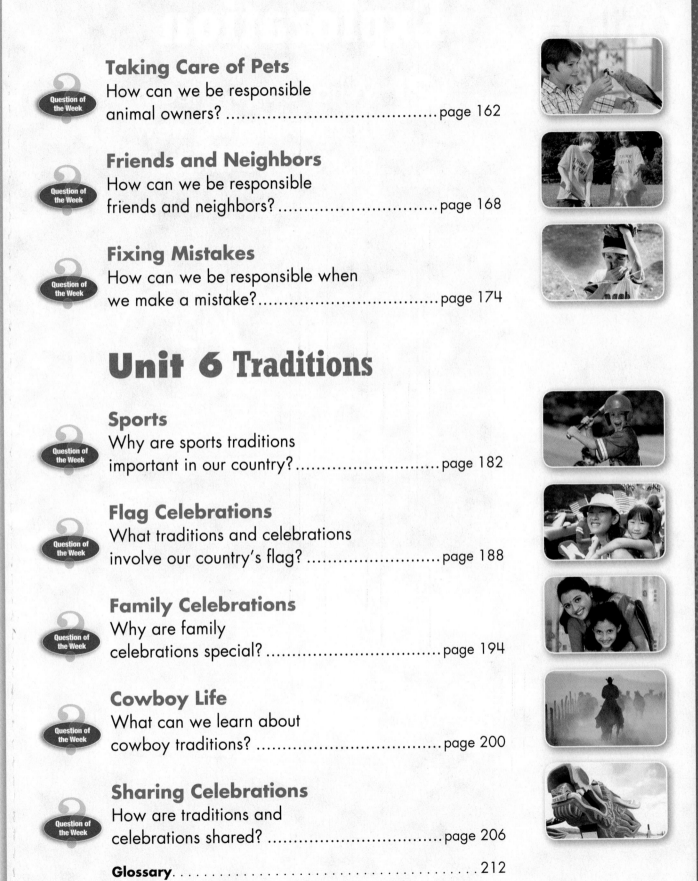

Get Online!

Hear it!
See it!
Do it!

- Big Question Video
- Concept Talk Video
- Envision It! Animation
- Grammar Jammer
- Daily Journal

Exploration

 What can we learn from exploring new places and things?

Exploring Communities
What can we learn by exploring different communities?

Exploring Space
What can we learn by exploring space?

Exploring Nature
What can we discover by exploring nature?

Before We Explore
How can we prepare for exploration?

Exploration's Answers
How does exploration help us find answers?

Exploration

PICTURE IT!

city

PICTURE IT!

country

PICTURE IT!

friends

busy
community
crops
different

What can we learn by exploring different communities?

The city has communities.
The country also has communities.
Different communities do things
in different ways. We can learn
from these differences.

Read the passage together.
Then circle the vocabulary words.

Communities

(Friends) live and work together in a community. A city community has many cars and busy streets. A country community has many farms, crops, and animals. People work in different ways in these communities. They can learn new things from each other.

Talk About It Complete the sentences below.

A city community has _____.
many cars, busy streets

A country community has _____.
many farms, crops and animals

Your Turn What can you tell about a city community? What can you tell about a country community? Tell a partner.

23

Describing We use words to tell about people. Special words help us tell what people look like and how they act.

Rachel looks excited.

Macy feels sad.

Peter is helpful.

Circle the words that tell about the children in the sentences above.

· ·

Talk About It Use special words to tell a partner about you.

I look _____.

I feel _____.

· ·

Your Turn What are some other words that tell about you? Tell a partner.

Character and Setting A **character** is a person in a story. A **setting** is the time and place where a story happens. When you read, look for words that tell about the characters and the setting.

Lucy lives in the country. There she can feed the animals and play in the fields. She loves to help with farm work. Lucy also likes to visit her aunt in the city. Life there is very different.

. . . .

Talk About It What can you tell about the character Lucy?

Lucy is _____.

. . . .

Your Turn Reread the passage above. What can you tell about the country setting?

Complete Sentences A **complete sentence** tells a complete thought. A complete sentence also ends with a period, question mark, or exclamation point.

My family lives in a city community.

period

Talk About It Draw a line under each complete sentence. Read the complete sentences with a partner.

A country community

A city is a community.

People live and work in a community.

Your Turn Finish the sentence frames below to make two complete sentences about your community.

My community is _____.

I like _____ in my community.

Think, Talk, and Write

city

Exploring Communities Think about city and country communities. Tell a partner how they are different. Then tell how your community is the same or different from a city or a country community.

country

- -

Talk About It Review the vocabulary on page 22. Tell or show a partner what each word means.

- -

Produce Language Write about a different community you want to explore. First draw a picture of the community you would like to explore. Complete the sentences. Then write in your Weekly Concept Journal.

I want to explore a _____ community.

I want to learn how people _____ in this community.

27

astronauts

shuttle

space

work
world

What can we learn by exploring space?

Astronauts work in space. They work hard to learn new things. They learn about space and about our world.

Read the passage together.
Then circle the vocabulary words.

Sally Ride

(Astronauts) explore space to learn new
things. Sally Ride is an astronaut.
She flew in the space shuttle.
She used the shuttle's robot
arm. She did work in space
to help us learn about
our world.

Talk About It Complete the sentences below.

Sally Ride _____.
is an astronaut, flew in the space shuttle

In space, Sally Ride _____.
did work, used the shuttle's robot arm

Your Turn Would you like to fly into
space? Why? Tell a partner.

Summarizing We use special words to tell the main points of a story. We might say *The story is about* or *The main idea is*.

For the story below, we could say:

The story is about Sammy. He wants to be an astronaut.

Sammy wants to travel to space someday.

He learns all he can about space. He works hard in school. He wants to be an astronaut.

· ·

Talk About It Tell a partner what the story above is about.

The main idea of the story is _____.

· ·

Your Turn Tell about a story you read.

The story is about _____.

Main Idea and Details The **main idea** is the most important idea in a story. The **details** tell us more about the main idea. When you read, look for the main idea and the details.

Astronauts study space.
Astronauts study the stars.
Astronauts study Earth too.
They learn about many places.

Talk About It Draw a line under the main idea. Tell the main idea to a partner.

The main idea is _____.

Your Turn Write two details that tell more about the main idea.

_____

_____

_____

31

Subjects The **subjects** of sentences are who or what the sentences are about. Every sentence has a subject.

Subject	Sentence
The space shuttle	**The space shuttle** traveled into space.
The astronaut	**The astronaut** rode into space.
Juanita	**Juanita** likes to look at the stars.

Talk About It Tell the subject in each sentence below. Circle the word or words.

Astronauts explore space.

Sally Ride is America's first woman astronaut.

Your Turn Write a sentence. Underline the subject.

_____

_____

stars

Exploring Space Think about how Sally Ride explored space. Tell a partner what astronauts learn about when they explore space.

moon

Talk About It Review the vocabulary on page 28. Tell or show a partner what each word means.

Produce Language Imagine you are an astronaut. Write what you would see as you explore space. First draw a picture of what you would see. Complete the sentences. Then write in your Weekly Concept Journal.

Astronauts work in _____.

I would see _____ while exploring space.

Vocabulary

PICTURE IT!

bear

PICTURE IT!

climb

PICTURE IT!

mother

far away
straight
take care

What can we discover by exploring nature?

Nature is exciting. We can learn about plants and animals. We can learn about how animals take care of each other.

Vocabulary in Context

Read the passage together.
Then circle the vocabulary words.

The Bears

Jack and his (mother) climb a hill in the woods. They see a mother bear and her baby cubs straight ahead. From far away, they watch the bear feed her cubs. Jack learns that bears take care of their baby cubs.

. . . .

Talk About It Complete the sentences.

Jack and his mom _____.
climb a hill, watch bears

Bears _____.
feed cubs, take good care of their baby cubs

. . . .

Your Turn What exciting things can we discover in nature? Tell a partner.

Literary Analysis In English, we usually first tell who or what the sentence is about. Then we say what the person or thing is or does.

Yes: The happy boy watched the animal.
No: Watched the animal the happy boy.

Talk About It Finish these sentences. Use words from the Word Box.

Word Box
Alejandro   ride   friend

My _____ walks to school with me.

Sara and Sam _____ bikes in the park.

_____ is afraid of bears.

Your Turn Write a sentence about a bear. Put the words in the correct order.

The bear _____

_____ .

Character, Setting, and Plot A **character** is the person or animal in a story. The **plot** is what happens in the story. The **setting** is when and where the story happens.

Characters	Plot	Setting
Jack, mother	First, Jack and his mother walk in the forest. Next, they see a brown rabbit. Last, Jack and his mother have a picnic lunch.	the forest lunchtime

Talk About It Look at the plot above. What happens first? Tell a partner.

Your Turn These pictures tell the plot of a story. Tell what happens at each part of the story.

First   Next   Last

Predicate The **predicate** is the word or group of words that tells something about the subject of the sentence. A predicate often shows an action.

Jack ⟨enjoys nature⟩.
The mother bear ⟨loves her cub⟩.
Han ⟨watches the leaves fall⟩.

Talk About It Read the sentences below. Underline the predicates.

We love the forest.

The animal ran through the woods.

Your Turn Finish the sentence below.

The deer _____

_____ .

Think, Talk, and Write

Exploring Nature Think about what Jack discovered by exploring nature with his mom. Tell a partner what we can discover when we explore different places in nature.

deer

bird

Talk About It Review the vocabulary on page 34. Tell or show a partner what each word means.

Produce Language Imagine you are exploring nature. Write about what you might find. First draw a picture of what you would see. Complete the sentences. Then write in your Weekly Concept Journal.

An animal I would see is _____.

I would also see _____ while exploring nature.

Vocabulary

first aid kit

hiking

water

planning

warm

How can we prepare for exploration?

Before we explore a new place, we need to do some planning. We need to think about what we need. We need to think about what we will find. This helps keep us safe. We must get ready!

Read the passage together.
Then circle the vocabulary words.

Getting Ready

We must do lots of (planning) before we
go hiking. We pack water and food.
We pack a first aid kit. We wear special
shoes and pack warm clothes. Good
planning will help us have a good trip.

· ·

Talk About It Complete the sentences below.

> Before we go hiking, we should _____.
> *plan; pack food, water, and clothes*
>
> We should bring _____.
> *warm clothes, a first aid kit*

· ·

Your Turn Why is it important to plan
well for a hike? Tell a partner.

41

Explaining We can use words and sentences to tell about people and things. Some words tell what a person does. A sentence may also tell why a person does something.

The actions are circled below. The reason for the action is underlined.

Miguel (wears) sturdy shoes to protect his feet.

Peggy (drinks) water to stay cool.

Talk About It Tell why you go to these places.

> I go to school to _____.
>
> I go to the playground to _____.

Your Turn What is something you do to get ready for school?

I _____ to get ready for school.

Main Idea and Details The **main idea** is the most important idea in a story. The **details** tell about the main idea.

Read the sentences below. Circle the main idea.

Kim plans a hike.

She packs a first aid kit.

Kim packs her camera too!

....

Talk About It What details tell about the main idea in the sentences above?

> The main idea is _____.
> Some details are _____.

....

Your Turn Reread the passage on page 41. Circle the main idea. Write it below. Write a detail that tells about the main idea.

_____

_____

Statements and Questions

A **statement** is a sentence that tells us something. A statement ends with a period. A **question** is a sentence that asks us something. A question ends with a question mark.

Question: Will you take your dog hiking**?**
Statement: Yes, we will take my dog hiking**.**

Talk About It Which sentence below is a statement? Which is a question? Talk with a partner.

Are you planning for your trip?

Yes, I am making a list.

Your Turn Write a statement and a question. Be sure to use the correct end punctuation for each sentence.

_____

_____

Think, Talk, and Write

Before We Explore Think about what you would need to do to prepare for a hiking trip. Tell a partner how you would prepare for a trip to a new place.

plan

pack

Talk About It Review the vocabulary on page 40. Tell or show a partner what each word means.

Produce Language Imagine you are going to explore a new place. Write how you would prepare. First draw a picture of what you would bring with you. Complete the sentences. Then write in your Weekly Concept Journal.

To prepare, I would _____.

I would bring _____ because _____.

Vocabulary

birds

butterflies

monkey

learn
much
teach

How does exploration help us find answers?

People explore to learn new things. We test our ideas when we explore. We can learn about plants, animals, and different places.

Read the passage together.
Then circle the vocabulary words.

Rain Forest Animals

Exploring the rain forest can (teach) us about animals. We might see a monkey. We might see birds. We might see butterflies. We can see how they all live together. We learn so much from exploring!

Talk About It Complete the sentences.

_____ live in the rain forest.
Birds, Butterflies, Monkeys

Exploring _____.
teaches us new things, teaches us about animals

Your Turn What kinds of animals can we find in a rain forest? Tell a partner.

Defining We can use words to help us group people, animals, places, and things. Grouping helps tell about kinds of things.

A gorilla
is an animal.

A parrot
is a bird.

A fern
is a plant.

Talk About It Look at the pictures below.
Tell a partner whether it is an animal or a bird.

This is _____.

This is _____.

Your Turn Name a group for the
picture on the right. Write it in a
sentence.

_____

_____

Classify and Categorize To **classify,** or **categorize,** means to put things that are alike into groups. When you read, watch for things that are alike.

A monkey belongs to the group called **animals.**

Some animals belong to the group called **birds.**

Flowers and trees belong to the group called **plants.**

Talk About It What are the three groups above? Tell a partner.

The groups are _____.

Your Turn Look at the passage on page 47. Name the animals you might find in a rain forest.

Rain Forest Animals

1. _____

2. _____

3. _____

Commands and Exclamations Some sentences, called **commands,** tell what to do. Commands end with a period. Some sentences, called **exclamations,** show surprise or excitement. Exclamation sentences end with an exclamation point.

> **Command:** Keep the rain forest clean**.**
>
> **Exclamation:** I love the rain forest**!**

Talk About It Decide whether each sentence below is a command or an exclamation. Put the correct punctuation after each sentence.

> I am very excited about exploring
>
> Our trip begins tomorrow
>
> Bring your backpack

Your Turn Think about a command you heard from your teacher today. Write it in a sentence.

_____

_____

Think, Talk, and Write

Exploration's Answers Think about what you would learn by exploring the rain forest. What could you see, hear, or touch? Tell a partner how exploring helps you learn new things.

cave

ocean

Talk About It Review the vocabulary on page 46. Tell or show a partner what each word means.

Produce Language Write about an animal or a place that you want to explore. First draw a picture of what you want to explore. Complete the sentences. Then write in your Weekly Concept Journal.

I want to explore _____.

Exploring _____ can teach me _____.

Get Online!

Hear it!
See it!
Do it!

- Big Question Video
- Concept Talk Video
- Envision It! Animation
- Grammar Jammer
- Daily Journal

Working Together

THE BIG ? How can we work together?

Helping People in Danger
How can we help each other in dangerous situations?

Changing History
How has working together changed history?

Meeting Needs
How can we work together to meet people's needs?

Working Together
Why is it a good idea to work together?

Solving Problems
How can we work together to solve problems?

Working Together

Vocabulary

PICTURE IT!

family

PICTURE IT!

firefighter

dangerous

listen

How can we help each other in dangerous situations?

People in a family can help each other. They can help when there is danger, like a fire. A family should have a plan for fires.

Read the passage together.
Then circle the vocabulary words.

Fire Plan

A fire plan can keep a (family) safe from dangerous fires. First, move away from the fire. Do not open warm doors. Leave the house if you can. Then, call 9-1-1. Listen to what the firefighter tells you.

Talk About It Complete the sentences below.

When there is a fire, you should first
_____ .

move away from the fire, leave the house

Next you should _____ .
call 9-1-1, listen to the firefighter

Your Turn What fire plan do you and your family have? Tell a partner about your fire plan.

Sequencing We use words to tell when things happen. *First, next,* and *last* are words that tell when things happen.

Circle the words that tell sequence in the sentences below.

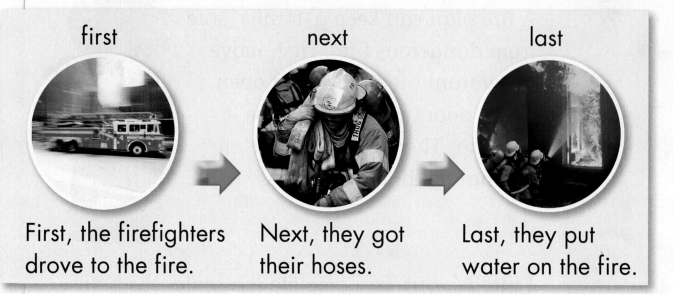

first   next   last

First, the firefighters drive to the fire.

Next, they got their hoses.

Last, they put water on the fire.

Talk About It Read these sentences with a partner. Circle the words that tell order.

First, I got out of the house.

Last, the firefighters came.

Next, I called 9-1-1.

Your Turn What is something else you do in order? Tell a partner. Use *first, next,* and *last.*

Sequence You can use special words, such as *first,* *next,* and *last,* to tell the **sequence,** or order, of events.

First, we learned about being safe.

Next, we made posters.

Last, we made a plan with our family.

Talk About It
Write the order of the sentences. Use *1, 2,* and *3.*

Next, write your plan. ___

First, tell your family about the plan. ___

Last, use your plan if there is a fire. ___

Your Turn Look at the pictures.
Write which happens first, next, and last.

_____   _____   _____

Nouns **Nouns** name people, places, and things.

a firefighter

a fire station

a fire hose

Talk About It Circle the nouns in these sentences. Tell a partner whether the noun names a person, a place, or a thing.

The house is on fire.

The mother helped.

The plan is on the wall.

Your Turn Choose a noun below to finish each sentence.

firefighter   hose

A _____ has water in it.

The _____ can help.

Think, Talk, and Write

Helping People in Danger
Think about how people can help each other in dangerous situations, like fires. Tell a partner what you would do if there is a fire.

get help

listen

Talk About It Review the vocabulary on page 54. Tell or show a partner what each word means.

Produce Language Write about how you and your family would help each other if you were in danger. First draw a picture of your plan. Complete the sentences. Then write in your Weekly Concept Journal.

First, my family would _____.

Next, we would _____.

PICTURE IT!

hurricane

PICTURE IT!

rebuild

**couldn't
damage
great
worst**

How has working together changed history?

People work together after storms, such as hurricanes. After a bad storm, people need to rebuild. Rebuilding can change history.

Read the passage together.
Then circle the vocabulary words.

Rebuilding

Katrina was a very bad (hurricane).
People couldn't believe how much
damage there was. The worst damage
was in New Orleans.
After Katrina, many
people helped
rebuild the city.
People were great.

Talk About It Complete the sentences below.

Katrina was a _____.
hurricane, storm

After Katrina, _____.
many people helped rebuild,
people were great

Your Turn How did people work
together after Hurricane Katrina?
What did they do? Tell a partner.

Describing We can use the verbs *am, is,* and *are* with words that tell how people look, act, and feel. See the examples below.

Circle the verb in each sentence below.

The boy is tired.

We are happy.

We are excited.

Talk About It Look at the picture. Describe the people.

The people are _____.

Your Turn Write a sentence about how you feel.

I am _____.

Author's Purpose An author is a person who writes something. Why do authors write? Authors write for many reasons. An author might write to tell a story or how he or she feels.

Read the paragraph below. Underline the describing words. Circle the verbs *am*, *is*, and *are*.

Today, I am sad. Hurricane Katrina damaged my house. The damage is bad. My mom and dad are sad too.

• •

Talk About It Why do you think the author wrote this? What does the author feel?

• •

Your Turn Look at the passage on page 61. Tell why you think the author wrote it.

_____

_____

_____

Grammar

Proper Nouns A **proper noun** names a special person, place, or thing. Proper nouns begin with capital letters, such as *A, B,* and *C.*

People	Places	Things
President Lincoln	California	Golden Gate Bridge
Elaine Rivera	Los Angeles	West Orange School
Doctor Moore	Main Street	Cool Clothes Company

Talk About It Circle the proper nouns.

Dr. Lopez

fire

San Diego

Your Turn Write a sentence about the city or town you live in. Remember to use capital letters!

I live in _____.

64

Think, Talk, and Write

cleaning up

building

Changing History Hurricanes and other storms cause damage. After these storms, people work together to fix the damage. Tell a partner what people can do to help.

Talk About It Review the vocabulary on page 60. Tell or show a partner what each word means.

Produce Language Write about how people can work together and change history after big storms like Hurricane Katrina. First draw a picture of what people can do. Complete the sentences. Then write in your Weekly Concept Journal.

Big storms can cause _____.

People can help to _____.

Vocabulary

community

tools

enough
work
whole

How can we work together to meet people's needs?

People need food, water, and a place to live. They also need a good community. People work together to make a good community.

Read the passage together.
Then circle the vocabulary words.

A Garden Grows!

People can (work) together to make a community garden. First, make sure enough people can help. Then, use tools to plant seeds in the whole area. Water the seeds. Finally, flowers will grow.

Talk About It Complete the sentences below.

People can work together to _____.
make a garden, plant seeds

To make a garden, you need _____.
tools, people

Your Turn Tell your partner about a time when you worked with other people to do something.

Asking Questions When we ask questions, we often use the words *who*, *what*, and *where*.

Circle the question words in the sentences below.

Who is planting seeds?

What is growing?

Where are the people?

Talk About It Ask your partner to respond to the questions below.

Who would help you plant some seeds?

What plants would you like to grow?

Where would you plant a garden?

Your Turn Ask your partner about a time he or she worked together for the community. Use *who*, *what*, and *where*.

Author's Purpose An author is a person who writes something. Authors write for different reasons. Sometimes authors answer questions when they write.

What Do You Need to Make a Garden?

To make a garden, you need soil. You need seeds. You also need sun and water.

Talk About It Read the paragraph above. What question is the author answering? Talk with a partner.

Your Turn Look at the passage on page 67. Why do you think the author wrote it?

_____

_____

_____

Singular and Plural Nouns A noun names a person, place, or thing. A **singular noun** names one person, place, or thing. A **plural noun** names more than one person, place, or thing.

Singular Nouns	Plural Nouns
girl	girls
garden	gardens
plant	plants

Talk About It Read these sentences. Circle the singular nouns. Underline the plural nouns.

Our garden is big.

There are many seeds.

We grow many plants.

Your Turn Finish these sentences. Use a singular noun and a plural noun from the chart above.

My sister is a _____.

All of the _____ are growing.

70

Think, Talk, and Write

Meeting Needs Think about how people work together to plant a community garden. People can work together to get other things they need too. Tell a partner how people work together to get what they need.

cooking

building

Talk About It Review the vocabulary on page 66. Tell or show a partner what each word means.

Produce Language Write about how people work together to get what they need. First draw a picture of people working together. Complete the sentences. Then write in your Weekly Concept Journal.

People need _____.

. People in a community can work together to _____.

Vocabulary

band

instruments

people

imagine
probably

Why is it a good idea to work together?

People often do things by themselves. Sometimes it is better to work together. One example of this is playing in a band.

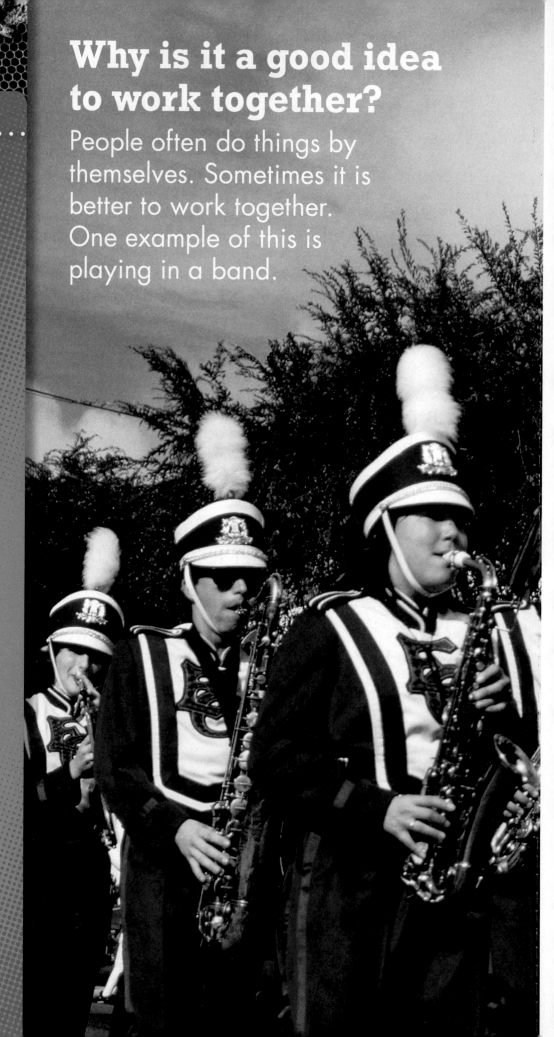

Read the passage together.
Then circle the vocabulary words.

Playing in a Band

(People) play instruments by themselves.
The music they make probably sounds
good. Imagine if there were a lot of
people playing instruments together.
In a band, people play instruments
together to make beautiful music.

Talk About It Complete the sentences below.

People _____.
play instruments, work together

In a band, _____.
people make beautiful music

Your Turn How do people in a
band work together? Tell a partner.

73

Sequencing We use words to tell the order, or sequence, of things. *Before* and *after* are words that help us tell when things happen.

Before	After

Before the girl played the instrument, she put the instrument together.

After the girl put the instrument together, she played the instrument.

Talk About It Tell what happened yesterday.

Before school, I _____ .

After school, I _____ .

Your Turn Look at the picture. Use *before* or *after* to complete this sentence.

_____ dinner, we make salad.

Sequence You can use special words to tell the order of events. When you read, look for words like *before* and *after*. They tell order. Circle the order words below.

After the band played, people clapped.

Before I played the drums, I played the piano.

. . . .

Talk About It Tell what is happening in these two pictures. Use the words *before* and *after*.

Before _____,

_____.

After _____,

_____.

. . . .

Your Turn Think of a time you helped your family. Write two sentences about what you did using the words *before* and *after*.

_____

_____

_____

_____

Plural Nouns **Plural nouns** name more than one person, place, or thing. Plural nouns usually end in -s. Many singular nouns that end in -s or -ch have plural forms that end in -es.

Circle the plural nouns in the sentences below.

Singular	Plural	Sentences
horn	horns	My horn was loud. All the horns were loud.
bus	buses	The band rode in a bus. We needed two buses.
bench	benches	The band sat on the bench. The band needed four benches.

Talk About It Which word is the plural noun in the sentence below? Tell your partner.

I will see four bands play tonight.

Your Turn Write the plural form of the word *instrument* in the sentence below.

Our _____ sound great together!

Think, Talk, and Write

Working Together People in a band can make music together. When people work together, they can do things that they couldn't do on their own. Tell a partner why it is a good idea to work together.

share work

have fun

Talk About It Review the vocabulary on page 72. Tell or show a partner what each word means.

Produce Language Write about why it is a good idea to work together. First draw a picture of people working together at home or at school. Complete the sentences. Then write in your Weekly Concept Journal.

People can work together to _____.

It is a good idea to work together because _____.

door

table

difficult
explained
minute

How can we work together to solve problems?

People can work together to solve problems. One person may be able to show another person something new.

Read the passage together.
Then circle the vocabulary words.

Homework Helpers

Lily thought math was (difficult). Phuong said he would help her. They sat at a table by the door. He explained that 60 seconds equals 1 minute. After they were done, Lily helped Phuong with spelling. They both liked helping!

Talk About It Complete the sentences below.

Lily _____.
thought math was difficult, helped Phuong

Lily and Phuong _____.
worked together, liked helping

Your Turn How have you helped someone? Tell a partner.

Comparing We can use words to tell how two things are alike and different. These words can tell size, color, or how something looks.

This group is **small.**

This group is **large.**

- -

Talk About It Look at these two books. Then complete the sentences using the words *big* and *small.*

This book is _____.

This book is _____.

- -

Your Turn Look at the books again. Write two sentences that tell how they are alike or different.

One book is _____.

The other book is _____.

Comparing Telling how two or more things are alike and different is called **comparing.** Clue words, such as *both, alike, like,* and *different,* are often used when comparing.

Read the sentences below. Circle the clue words.

The girls are alike because they both are eating a snack.

The girls are different because one girl has curly hair and one girl has straight hair.

. . . .

Talk About It Say a sentence that compares these two pictures. Use *alike, like,* or *different* in your sentence.

The pictures are alike because _____.

The pictures are different because _____.

. . . .

Your Turn Read the passage on page 79. Compare Lily and Phuong.

Lily and Phuong are alike because _____.

Lily and Phuong are different because _____.

Grammar

Possessive Nouns A noun names a person, place, or thing. A **possessive noun** names a person, place, or thing that owns something. You can make possessive nouns by adding -'s to nouns.

Noun	Possessive Noun
(Maya) has lost her spelling book.	(Maya's) spelling book is lost.
My (school) has a big lunchroom.	My (school's) lunchroom is big.

Talk About It Read the sentences below to a partner. Circle the possessive nouns.

The girls had bicycles.
One girl's bicycle was green.

Charlie's friend helped him tie his shoelaces.

Your Turn Write a sentence with a possessive noun.

_____

_____

Think, Talk, and Write

Solving Problems Some things are difficult to do. Think about how Lily and Phuong helped each other. Tell a partner how people can work together to solve problems.

explain

show

· ·

Talk About It Review the vocabulary on page 78. Tell or show a partner what each word means.

· ·

Produce Language Write about how you helped someone solve a problem. First draw a picture showing how you helped. Complete the sentences. Then write in your Weekly Concept Journal.

To solve problems, people can _____.

I helped by _____.

Get Online!

Hear it!
See it!
Do it!

- Big Question Video
- Concept Talk Video
- Envision It! Animation
- Grammar Jammer
- Daily Journal

Creative Ideas

THE BIG ?

What does it mean
to be creative?

Helping with Creative Ideas

When does support from others help with a creative idea?

Sharing Ideas

In what creative ways do we communicate?

Creative Ways to Solve Problems

How can creative thinking solve a problem?

Surprising Ideas

When does a creative idea lead to a surprise?

The Start of Ideas

Where do creative ideas come from?

Creative Ideas

Vocabulary

buckets

river

creative
pretty
village

When does support from others help with a creative idea?

Many people have creative ideas for doing or making something. Sometimes people need help with their creative ideas.

Read the passage together.
Then circle the vocabulary words.

The River

Juan lived in a (village) by a pretty river.
The village needed water. Juan had a
creative idea to get water from the river.
He asked people to fill buckets and then
pass them to each other.

Talk About It Complete the sentences.

Juan lived _____.
in a village, by a river

The village people _____.
*used buckets to get water,
passed buckets to each other*

Your Turn What is Juan's creative idea?
Tell a partner.

Comparing We use words to tell how things are alike. The word *like* helps us tell how two things are alike.

The dog is small.   The cat is small.

The dog is **like** the cat.

. . . .

Talk About It Tell a partner how the shirt and rug in the sentences below are alike.

The shirt is striped. The rug is striped.
The shirt is _____ like the rug.

. . . .

Your Turn What are two things you can compare? Tell a partner.

Compare and Contrast When we **compare,** we tell how two or more things are alike. When we **contrast,** we tell how two or more things are different.

The river has water.
The river is long.

The lake has water.
The lake is round.

The river is **like** the lake.
The river is also **not like** the lake.

Talk About It How is a river like a lake?
How is a river not like a lake? Tell a partner.

Your Turn Juan was helpful in the story on page 87.
How is Juan like someone else you know about?

_____ is like Juan because

_____ .

Verbs A word that shows an action is a **verb.** A verb tells what the subject of a sentence is doing.

Juan **runs** to the river.

The people **pass** buckets of water.

Talk About It Circle the verbs in each sentence below.

The woman pours the water.
Juan carries the bucket.

Your Turn Fill in the blanks with one of the following verbs.

lifts   swims   walks

The girl _____ to the river.

She _____ in the water.

He _____ the bucket.

Think, Talk, and Write

Helping with Creative Ideas

The people in Juan's village helped with his creative idea. Look at the picture. What creative idea do the people in this village use so their houses do not get wet from the river? Tell a partner.

raised houses

Talk About It
Review the vocabulary on page 86. Tell or show a partner what each word means.

Produce Language
Write about a time when someone helped you do or make something. First draw a picture of your idea. Complete the sentences. Then write in your Weekly Concept Journal.

My idea was _____.

_____ helped me by _____.

Sharing Ideas

Vocabulary

artist

sunrise

water lilies

communicate
paint
show

In what creative ways do we communicate?

People communicate their ideas in many ways. One creative way is to paint. People can paint to show how they feel about something.

Read the passage together.
Then circle the vocabulary words.

Painting

Monet was an (artist). He lived long ago.
He would paint pictures to communicate.
His paintings show beautiful colors. One
famous picture shows a sunrise. Another
picture shows water lilies. Water lilies are
flowers on the water.

Talk About It Complete the sentences.

> Monet _____ .
> *was an artist, lived long ago*
>
> The paint colors _____ .
> *are beautiful, look like a sunrise*

Your Turn What do you think Monet was
saying with his pictures? Tell a partner.

Interpreting We use words to tell what we think something means. The words *I think* help us communicate what we see.

I think this painting shows how the sun sets.

I think this painting shows a field of flowers.

. . . .

Talk About It Look at this painting. Tell what you think it communicates.

I think the painting shows _____.

. . . .

Your Turn What does this painting communicate?

_____

_____

_____

Draw Conclusions You use what you read or see and what you know to **draw conclusions.** Then you explain why you made those conclusions.

Monet painted many lakes and fields. His paintings made the lakes and fields look beautiful.

What conclusion can you draw from the paragraph above?

· ·

Talk About It Read the paragraph above. Look at the picture. Draw a conclusion with a partner.

> I think Monet _____ .

· ·

Your Turn Write a sentence about this painting. Draw a conclusion and explain why.

_____

_____

_____

Nouns and Verbs A **noun** names a person, place, or thing. A **verb** can show action.

Circle the verbs and underline the nouns in the sentences below.

Sentence	Nouns	Verbs
Diego hugs his dog.	Diego, dog	hugs
Mai paints many trees.	Mai, trees	paints

Talk About It Circle the verbs and underline the nouns in the sentences below.

Ana paints a car.

Our friends buy the picture.

The paintings tell a story.

Your Turn Write a verb in the blanks below.

She _____ a picture of a flower.

He _____ the apple red.

They _____ pictures of kittens.

Think, Talk, and Write

singing

dancing

Sharing Ideas Monet communicated his ideas by painting. People show what they feel in different ways. Tell a partner some other creative ways that people communicate.

Talk About It Review the vocabulary on page 92. Tell or show a partner what each word means.

Produce Language Write about a creative way that people communicate. First draw a picture of a way a person can communicate. Complete the sentences. Then write in your Weekly Concept Journal.

People can communicate by _____.

They can use _____ to show how they feel.

Creative Ways to Solve Problems

Vocabulary

suitcases

wheels

heavy
solve
today
whatever

How can creative thinking solve a problem?

Sometimes a person has a problem that needs to be solved. People who have creative ideas can help solve that problem.

Read the passage together.
Then circle the vocabulary words.

Suitcases

When people go on trips, they use (suitcases) to pack whatever they need. Suitcases can be very heavy. A man wanted to solve that problem. He attached tiny wheels to suitcases. Today, people can roll the heavy suitcases!

· ·

Talk About It Complete the sentences.

> Suitcases _____.
> *can be very heavy, can be rolled today*
>
> People _____.
> *go on trips, use suitcases*

· ·

Your Turn What problem did the man solve? How did he solve it? Tell a partner.

Cause-and-Effect Relationship We can use words like *because* to tell why things happen.

She is happy **because** her suitcase has wheels.

He is wet **because** he forgot his umbrella.

Talk About It Look at the picture. Use the word *because* to tell what happened and why.

Your Turn Tell about something that happened to you today. Tell why it happened.

Cause and Effect Things you read often tell about something that happens. This is called an **effect.** The **cause** is why something happens. The word *because* is a clue word. It tells the cause of something.

He cannot carry the suitcase **because** it is too heavy.

The suitcase is easy to pull **because** it has wheels.

. . . .

Talk About It Read each sentence above. What is the cause? What is the effect? Tell a partner.

Cause	_____		Effect	_____

. . . .

Your Turn Look at the passage on page 99. What caused the man to put wheels on suitcases?

_____

_____

101

Verbs A **verb** can tell an action. Verbs can tell what happened in the past, what happens today or in the present, or what will happen in the future.

Past	Sandra **solved** a problem.
Present	Sandra **solves** a problem.
Future	Sandra **will solve** a problem.

Talk About It Circle the verbs.

Todd will pack his suitcase tomorrow.

Hannah looked for her suitcase in the closet.

Roberto carries his suitcase to the car.

Your Turn Tell whether each sentence happened in the past, is happening in the present, or will happen in the future.

Laura travels on an airplane.

Suvrat traveled to California last week.

Cindy will travel to New York next month.

baskets

stroller

Creative Ways to Solve Problems

There are many ways to solve problems. Look at the pictures. Tell a partner how creative thinking helped to solve this problem.

- -

Talk About It Review the vocabulary on page 98. Tell or show a partner what each word means.

- -

Produce Language Write about a creative way to solve the problem of carrying something heavy. First draw a picture of the creative solution. Complete the sentences. Then write in your Weekly Concept Journal.

It is hard to carry heavy _____.

A creative way to solve this problem is to use _____.

Vocabulary

sculpture

stone

tiger

instead
many
surprised

When does a creative idea lead to a surprise?

A person starts with a creative idea. As the person works, the idea can change. This is how many creative ideas become a surprise.

Read the passage together.
Then circle the vocabulary words.

The Sculpture

Marco was making a (sculpture) from stone. Marco had seen a statue of a tiger. He wanted to make a statue of a tiger too. He worked for many hours. Marco was surprised to see that his tiger was small. He would make it a cat instead!

Talk About It Complete the sentences.

Marco was _____.
making a sculpture, working

The tiger _____.
was a sculpture, was small

Your Turn Why was Marco surprised?
Tell a partner.

Making Predictions We use words to tell what we think will happen in the future. Look for the phrase *is going to*.

Ian **is going to** make a sculpture.

The sculpture **is going to** look like a dog.

Talk About It Look at the picture. What do you think is going to happen?

Your Turn What do you think is going to happen when you get home from school? Tell a partner.

Theme and Plot A **plot** is what happens in the beginning, the middle, and the end of a story. Every story has one "big idea" or **theme.**

The theme, or big idea, below is that giving a person a picture can make them happy.

Jon drew a picture of a dog. He gave it to his friend. His friend was very happy.

Talk About It Look at the pictures. Tell your partner what the big idea is and what the girl might do next.

Your Turn Which sentence below tells the plot of the passage on page 105? Which sentence tells the theme?

A boy makes a sculpture.

Surprises come from creative ideas.

Verbs **Verbs** can tell what happened in the past.
Verbs can tell what happens in the present.
Verbs can tell what will happen in the future.

Past	Corey **painted** a picture yesterday.
Present	Corey **paints** a picture today.
Future	Corey **will paint** a picture tomorrow.

Talk About It Circle the verbs in each sentence.

Jacob created a sculpture yesterday.

Maria will make a clay tiger tomorrow.

Lauren walks to art class today.

Your Turn Write something you did yesterday.
Write something you will do tomorrow.

_____

_____

_____

drawing

Surprising Ideas Many creative ideas can lead to a surprise. Think about a time when you started drawing or creating something and then your idea changed. Tell a partner about the surprise.

painting

Talk About It Review the vocabulary on page 104. Tell or show a partner what each word means.

Produce Language Write about a time when you started to make something and then your idea changed. First draw a picture of the new thing you made. Complete the sentences. Then write in your Weekly Concept Journal.

I started to make a _____.

Instead, I made a _____.

The Start of Ideas

Vocabulary

burrs

clothes

touch fastener

easier
hours
invent

Where do creative ideas come from?

Creative ideas come from many places. Some creative ideas come from what we observe, or see. Creative ideas can even come from nature.

Read the passage together.
Then circle the vocabulary words.

A Creative Idea

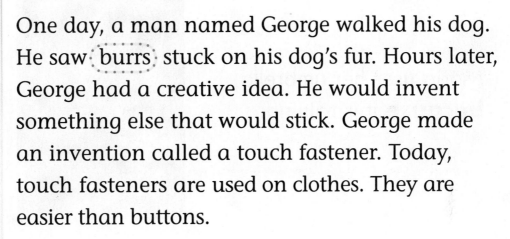

One day, a man named George walked his dog.
He saw (burrs) stuck on his dog's fur. Hours later,
George had a creative idea. He would invent
something else that would stick. George made
an invention called a touch fastener. Today,
touch fasteners are used on clothes. They are
easier than buttons.

· ·

Talk About It Complete the sentences.

A touch fastener is _____.
a creative invention, easier than buttons

The creative idea _____.
*came from nature, came from seeing burrs
on a dog.*

· ·

Your Turn Where did George's creative
idea come from? Tell a partner.

Cause-and-Effect Relationship We use words to tell why things happen. Words such as *because* tell why.

Maria uses her umbrella **because** it is raining.

· ·

Talk About It Think about a simple object you use every day, such as a pencil. Why do you think that object was invented? Use the word *because*. Tell a partner.

· ·

Your Turn Look at the picture. Why did the egg break? Talk about it with a partner.

Cause and Effect We read about things that happen. The thing that happens is the **effect.** Why the thing happens is the **cause.**

Cause: George found burrs on the dog's fur.

Effect: George invents a touch fastener.

Talk About It What is the cause of George's invention? What is the effect? Tell a partner.

Your Turn Read the sentence below. Tell the cause and effect.

This dog is sleeping because he played all day.

Cause: _____

Effect: _____

Verbs **Verbs** can tell what happens in the present. Verbs can also tell what happened in the past.

Past	Present
I **was** at home.	I **am** at school.
He **was** very sad.	He **is** very happy.
They **were** playing outside.	They **are** playing inside.

- -

Talk About It Find the verb in each sentence.

George is creative.

The dog was fast.

These sneakers are new.

- -

Your Turn Write a verb that completes each sentence.

I _____ very excited.

The art fair _____ today.

We _____ very surprised.

I _____ proud of my idea.

Think, Talk, and Write

The Start of Ideas Think about how George's idea for a touch fastener came from seeing burrs stuck to his dog. Where do you think creative ideas come from? Tell a partner.

discussing

observing

Talk About It Review the vocabulary on page 110. Tell or show a partner what each word means.

Produce Language Think about something you could invent. Write about your idea. First draw a picture of your invention. Complete the sentences. Then write in your Weekly Concept Journal.

I would invent a _____.

I got this idea by _____.

Our Changing World

How do things change? How do they stay the same?

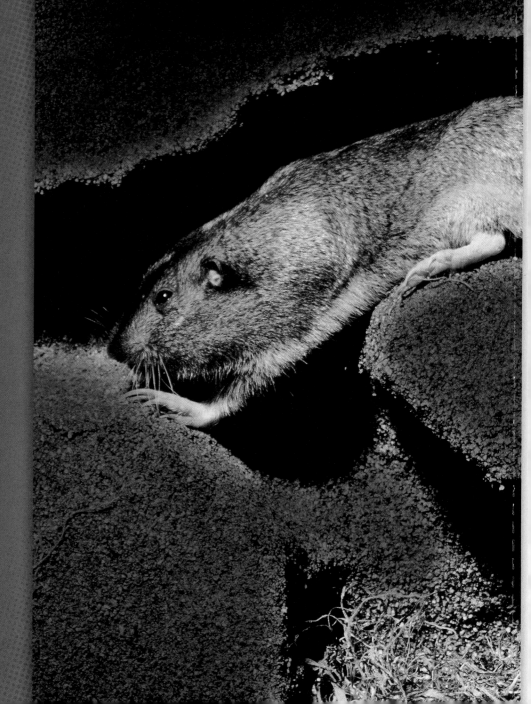

Life Changes
How can familiar things help us with changes?

Plant Changes
How do plants change over time?

Changes Under the Ground
What changes occur under the ground?

New Changes
Why are some changes difficult?

Weather Changes
How do changes in the weather affect us?

Our Changing World

Life Changes

Vocabulary

PICTURE IT!

bundle

PICTURE IT!

quilt

strange
wrapped

How can familiar things help us with changes?

Sometimes things change. We might not want them to change. Things we know can help us with change. Old things can help us be happy in a new home.

Read the passage together.
Then circle the vocabulary words.

Grandma's Surprise

Ana was sad because she was moving to a (strange) new place. Before Ana left, Grandma came to visit. She had a large, wrapped bundle. It was Ana's grandmother's quilt! Grandma thought that the quilt would help Ana feel better in her new home.

· ·

Talk About It Complete the sentences below.

Grandma _____.
came to visit, gave Ana her quilt

The quilt _____.
was wrapped in a bundle, would help Ana feel better

· ·

Your Turn What would you take with you if you moved to a new home? Tell a partner.

119

Comparing and Contrasting We use words, such as *like* and *unlike,* to tell how things are the same or different.

The plate is **like** the cup because they are both red.

The bowl is **unlike** the cup and the plate because it is blue.

. . . .

Talk About It Use the word *like* or *unlike* to compare these boxes. Tell a partner.

. . . .

Your Turn Find two things in your classroom that are alike. Find two things that are different.

_____ is like _____

because _____ .

_____ is unlike _____

because _____ .

Compare and Contrast When you **compare** two or more things, you tell how those things are alike. When you **contrast** things, you tell how those things are different. Sometimes what we read compares and contrasts.

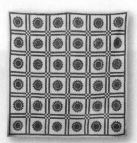

The two quilts are **like** each other beause they both are yellow.

The third quilt is **unlike** the other two because it is not yellow.

Talk About It Tell how the houses are alike. Tell how they are different.

The houses are like each other because _____.

The houses are unlike each other because _____.

Your Turn Look at the pictures of houses. What is another way that the houses are alike and different? Tell a partner.

Adjectives Words that describe people, places, and things are called **adjectives.**

happy girl   **tall** buildings   **hot** fireplace

Talk About It Choose an adjective to tell about the boy.

He is a _____ boy.

Your Turn Choose an adjective from below to complete each sentence.

happy   sad   red   blue

The _____ girl unpacked the box.

We put the _____ quilt on the bed.

Think, Talk, and Write

favorite toys

Life Changes Think about how Ana's grandmother's quilt helped her feel better when she moved. Tell a partner how having things we know near us can help us with difficult changes.

photos

Talk About It Review the vocabulary on page 118. Tell or show a partner what each word means.

Produce Language Write about a special thing that you have. Tell how it helps you with change. First draw a picture of the thing. Complete the sentences. Then write in your Weekly Concept Journal.

A special thing I have is _____.

It helps me because _____.

123

PICTURE IT!

blossoms

PICTURE IT!

soil

autumn
harvest
seed

How do plants change over time?

A plant begins as a seed in the ground. After it is watered, it begins to grow. Soon, the stem comes out of the ground. The plant changes from a seed into a plant.

Read the passage together.
Then circle the vocabulary words.

Apple Trees

An apple tree begins as a (seed) that
is planted in the soil. It grows, and
in the spring, you can see leaves
and blossoms. In the summer,
the apples grow. In autumn,
the apples are ready to harvest.
People pull the apples off the
trees and eat them.

Talk About It Complete the sentences below.

In the spring, the apple tree has _____.
leaves, blossoms

In autumn, the apples _____.
are ready to harvest, are eaten

Your Turn How does an apple
tree change? Tell a partner.

Describing We use words to tell about people, places, and things.

The describing words are circled below.

The tree is (small).
It has (red) apples.

The tree is (big).
The leaves are (green).

Talk About It Use describing words to tell about an apple.

> The apple is _____.
>
> It is _____.

Your Turn What did you eat for dinner last night? Use describing words to tell a friend.

Details and Facts **Facts** are pieces of information that are true. **Details** tell more about facts. The sentences below tell details about an apple tree.

An apple tree changes during the year. In the spring, there are blossoms on the tree. In the fall, there are apples on the tree.

Talk About It Read the sentences above. Then tell a partner a detail about an apple tree.

Your Turn What happens to an apple tree in the fall? Write a sentence.

_____

_____

Adjectives An **adjective** gives a detail to describe a noun.

five oranges   **small** grapes   a **round** pumpkin

Talk About It
Tell your partner which words are the adjectives in each sentence.

Two girls dance.

I see a tall tree.

There is a square clock.

Your Turn Write an adjective to describe each picture.

_____   _____   _____

128

Think, Talk, and Write

bean plant

Plant Changes Think about how an apple tree grows from a seed and changes over time. Tell a partner how plants grow and change.

orange tree

Talk About It Review the vocabulary on page 124. Tell or show a partner what each word means.

Produce Language Write about how plants, like apple and orange trees, grow and change. First draw a picture of how a plant grows and changes. Complete the sentences. Then write in your Weekly Concept Journal.

A plant begins as a _____.

As it grows you can see _____.

Changes Under the Ground

Vocabulary

PICTURE IT!
badger

PICTURE IT!
claws

burrow
tunnels
underground

What changes occur under the ground?

If you were able to look underground, you would see many things. You might see animals. You might see badgers digging tunnels.

Read the passage together.
Then circle the vocabulary words.

Underground Home

A (badger) uses its claws to dig for food.
They can dig through soil. They can even
dig underground tunnels in the soil.
They can also dig an underground burrow
for sleeping. Their digging changes
the earth underground.

Talk About It Complete
the sentences below.

> Badgers use their claws to _____.
> *dig for food, dig tunnels*
>
> Badgers dig underground _____.
> *burrows, for sleeping*

Your Turn Tell your partner
two facts about badgers.

Describing We use special words to tell the location of people, places, and things.

The badger is **below** the ground.

The badger is **above** the ground.

The tunnel is **under** the ground.

The words *below, above,* and *under* tell where something is in each picture above.

· ·

Talk About It Use one of the location words above to fill in the sentence.

The badger is digging _____ the ground.

· ·

Your Turn Write a sentence that describes where something is in your classroom. Use the word *above, below,* or *under.*

_____

_____

Graphic Sources A **graphic source** is a picture, or diagram, that can help you learn new things.

The picture can help you understand the words.

—— leaves

—— trunk

—— roots

Talk About It Point to each label.
Say each part of the tree.

Your Turn Complete the sentences below.

The roots are _____ the ground.

The trunk is _____ the ground.

The roots are _____ the trunk.

Adjectives That Compare

Adjectives are words that describe. They can also compare people, places, and things. When you use **adjectives that compare,** you add *-er* to compare two things. You add *-est* to compare more than two things.

The girl is **tall.**
The boy is **taller** than the girl.
The woman is the **tallest.**

Talk About It Look at the picture above. Use the adjective *bigger* to compare the woman and the boy. Tell a partner.

Your Turn Write a sentence about the badgers using the word *larger*.

_____

_____

Think, Talk, and Write

Changes Under the Ground

Think about what badgers do underground. Tell a partner what animals like badgers do underground.

digging

eating

Talk About It Review the vocabulary on page 130. Tell or show a partner what each word means.

Produce Language Write about how animals like badgers can change the earth underground. First draw a picture of the animal underground. Complete the sentences. Then write in your Weekly Concept Journal.

Animals like badgers can change the _____.

They dig in the soil and _____.

Vocabulary

PICTURE IT!

town

PICTURE IT!

unhappy

attend
enjoy
fair
move

Why are some changes difficult?

Sometimes things change. Sometimes we're unhappy when something changes. The changes can make you sad. One of these changes may be going to a new school.

Read the passage together.
Then circle the vocabulary words.

A NEW SCHOOL

Ben thought it wasn't (fair) that his
family had to move to a new town.
Now he would have to attend a
new school. He was unhappy
because he didn't think he
would enjoy his new school or
make new friends. But he was wrong!

Talk About It Complete the sentences below.

Ben had to _____.
move to a new town, attend a new school

Ben was unhappy because
he didn't think _____.
*he would make new friends, he would
enjoy his new school*

Your Turn Tell a partner why Ben
thought moving was not fair.

Describing Sometimes we use action words to describe.

Action Word	Using the Action Word to Describe
move	The family is **moving** to a new home.
walk	The boy is **walking** to school.

· ·

Talk About It Use the action word in parentheses to describe.

(talk) Our teacher is _____.

(laugh) The children are _____.

· ·

Your Turn Look at the picture.
Use an action word to describe.

The girl is _____.

138

Plot What happens at the beginning, middle, and end of a story is its **plot.**

Maya moved to her new home. She was sad because she missed her friends. But at her new school, she made new friends. She was happy.

This chart shows the plot of the story above.

Beginning	Maya moves to her new home.
Middle	Maya misses her friends.
End	Maya makes new friends at school.

Talk About It Retell the plot of the story above.

Your Turn Draw pictures to show the plot of a story you know.

Beginning	Middle	End

Adverbs An **adverb** tells more about an action word. It often tells when or where.

When:
I will go to my new school **tomorrow.**
I will go to school **early.**

Where:
I will sit in the seat **there.**
You will sit in the seat **here.**

Talk About It Use the following adverbs to complete the sentences below: *there, late.*

The school bus picked me up _____.

My new friend lives _____.

Your Turn Write a sentence using one of the following adverbs: *yesterday, here, soon, there.*

_____

_____

Think, Talk, and Write

New Changes Think about how Ben didn't want to go to his new school. Tell a partner why some changes are difficult.

new house

new school

Talk About It Review the vocabulary on page 136. Tell or show a partner what each word means.

Produce Language Write about a difficult change. Tell how you felt. First draw a picture of the change you had to make. Complete the sentences. Then write in your Weekly Concept Journal.

A difficult change I had to make was _____.

I felt _____.

branches

picnic

outside
soon
weather

How do changes in the weather affect us?

The weather affects what we can or can't do outside. If it's sunny or rainy, there are things you can do and things you can't do.

Read the passage together.
Then circle the vocabulary words.

Stormy Weather

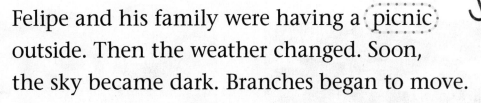

Felipe and his family were having a (picnic)
outside. Then the weather changed. Soon,
the sky became dark. Branches began to move.

"The weather is changing!" said Dad.

"Let's go home before it rains!" said Mom.

"Grab the blankets," said Dad.

Talk About It Complete the sentences below.

When the weather changed, _____.
the sky became dark, the branches moved

Dad said, "_____!"
The weather is changing

Your Turn Tell your partner why
Felipe and his family had to go home.

Evaluating Sometimes we use words to tell about many things that are the same. We can use words, such as *each* and *every,* to talk about things that are the same.

Every person has an umbrella.

Each umbrella has a circle on it.

Talk About It Look at the picture and fill in the blank.

_____ child is wearing a raincoat.

Your Turn Look at the picture and write a sentence that uses *each* or *every.*

_____

_____

_____

Details and Facts **Facts** are pieces of information that are true. **Details** can tell more about facts. The sentences below tell details about a rainstorm.

The rain fell heavily outside. It was a big storm. There were dark gray clouds. Emma was sad. She could not play ball outside.

. . . .

Talk About It Read the sentences above. Then tell a partner a detail about the rainstorm.

. . . .

Your Turn How did Emma feel about the rainstorm? Write a sentence.

_____

_____

Adverbs An **adverb** tells more about an action word. It often tells how someone does something.

The girl ran **quickly** in the rain.

The boy walked **carefully** up the stairs.

Talk About It Read the sentences. Circle the words that tell how.

The wind blew noisily.

The snow fell softly.

Your Turn Write a sentence about the weather, using an adverb that tells how.

_____

_____

146

Think, Talk, and Write

sunny

rainy

Weather Changes Think about how the weather affected what Felipe and his family were doing. Tell a partner how the weather can affect what you do outside.

Talk About It Review the vocabulary on page 142. Tell or show a partner what each word means.

Produce Language Write about how a change in the weather affected something you did. First draw a picture of the weather. Complete the sentences. Then write in your Weekly Concept Journal.

At first the weather was _____ .

Then it was _____ .

When the weather changed, I _____ .

Get Online!

Hear it!
See it!
Do it!

- Big Question Video
- Concept Talk Video
- Envision It! Animation
- Grammar Jammer
- Daily Journal

Responsibility

THE BIG ?

What does it mean to be responsible?

Doing a Good Job
Why should we be responsible for doing a good job?

Helping Our Community
How can we be responsible community members?

Taking Care of Pets
How can we be responsible animal owners?

Friends and Neighbors
How can we be responsible friends and neighbors?

Fixing Mistakes
How can we be responsible when we make a mistake?

Responsibility

Vocabulary

PICTURE IT!
ambulance

PICTURE IT!
fire truck

operator
quickly
responsible

Why should we be responsible for doing a good job?

People are responsible when they do a good job. We can trust people who are responsible. We can count on them to help us.

Read the passage together.
Then circle the vocabulary words.

Calling 9-1-1

Jill is a 9-1-1 operator. She helps people who call 9-1-1. Is there a fire? Jill will send a fire truck quickly. Is someone hurt? Jill will send an ambulance quickly. Jill is responsible for saving lives.

Talk About It Complete the sentences.

Jill is _____.
an operator, responsible for saving lives

People can call 9-1-1 when _____.
there is a fire, someone is hurt

Your Turn Why is Jill responsible?
Tell a partner.

151

Describing We use words to tell about actions. Some of these words end in *-ly*.

The fire truck comes **quickly.**

The firefighter speaks **loudly.**

Talk About It
Say which words tell about actions.

The 9-1-1 operator talks calmly.

The fire burns brightly.

Firefighters run bravely.

Your Turn Use *quickly* in a sentence.
Tell your sentence to a partner.

Main Idea and Details A **main idea** is the most important idea in a story. **Details** tell about a main idea. The first sentence in the paragraph below is the main idea. The rest are details.

Firefighters are responsible for helping people. One firefighter runs quickly. Another firefighter aims a hose.

. . . .

Talk About It What is the main idea in the paragraph above? What are two details?

. . . .

Your Turn Look at the passage on page 151. What is the main idea?

_____

_____

_____

Pronouns A **pronoun** takes the place of the name of a person, place, or thing. The chart below shows pronouns.

I am doing a good job.
He is responsible.
She is responsible.
It is a big fire.

We are doing a good job.
You are responsible.
They are firefighters.

Talk About It Circle the pronoun in each sentence.

She is a firefighter.

I ride on the fire truck.

We will call 9-1-1.

Your Turn Complete each sentence. Use a pronoun from the box at the top of the page.

_____ are 9-1-1 operators.

_____ is a fire truck.

firefighters

Doing a Good Job Think about how Jill is a responsible 9-1-1 operator. People count on her to help them. Tell a partner why it is important to do a good job.

nurse

Talk About It Review the vocabulary on page 150. Tell or show a partner what each word means.

Produce Language Write about a time when you did a good job at home or at school. First draw a picture of what you were doing. Complete the sentences. Then write in your Weekly Concept Journal.

I did a good job when I _____.

It is important to be responsible because _____.

Vocabulary

bags

boxes

members
repack
unpack

How can we be responsible community members?

People live and work together in a community. People take care of one another. People help one another.

Read the passage together.
Then circle the vocabulary words.

Food Drive

(Members) of the community are having a food drive. First, people bring in bags of food. Next, workers unpack the bags. They repack the food into boxes. Last, workers give the boxes to people who need food.

Talk About It Complete the sentences.

The workers _____.
unpack the bags, repack the food into boxes, give boxes of food to people

The community members _____.
have food drives, help each other

Your Turn How is the community being responsible? Tell a partner.

Sequencing We use words to tell sequence, or the order of when things happen. Special words help us tell things in order.

First, get some food.

Next, put the food in a bag.

Last, take the bag to the food drive.

Talk About It Tell how you can give food to a food drive.

First, I _____.

Next, I _____.

Last, I _____.

Your Turn What is something else you do in order? Tell a partner what you do first, next, and last.

Steps in a Process A process is something we do. It can take many steps to finish a process. The words *first, next,* and *last* help us tell the **steps in a process.**

First, people bring food to the food drive.

Next, workers sort the food.

Last, workers give the food to other people.

Talk About It What do the workers do first? What do they do next? What do they do last?

Your Turn These pictures show a park being cleaned up. They are not in order. Tell what happens first, next, and last.

Singular and Plural Pronouns **Singular pronouns** stand for one person, place, or thing. **Plural pronouns** stand for more than one person, place, or thing.

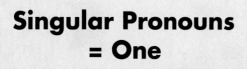

Singular Pronouns = One	Plural Pronouns = More than One
I, you, he, she, it	we, you, they

Talk About It Circle the pronouns.
Tell whether the pronouns are singular or plural.

They have a food drive.

She gives food to people.

Your Turn Write pronouns in the chart.

Singular Pronouns	Plural Pronouns

Think, Talk, and Write

Helping Our Community People do things, such as have food drives, to help people in their community. Tell a partner why it is important to be a responsible community member.

cleaning up

giving

Talk About It Review the vocabulary on page 156. Tell or show a partner what each word means.

Produce Language Write about something you can do to help your community. First draw a picture of what you can do. Complete the sentences. Then write in your Weekly Concept Journal.

I can help my community by _____.

It is important to help my community because

_____.

Vocabulary

PICTURE IT!

cage

PICTURE IT!

parrot

forgot
knows
owners
safe

How can we be responsible animal owners?

Many people are animal owners. They keep animals as pets. People must give their pets food, water, and a safe place to live.

Read the passage together.
Then circle the vocabulary words.

Brett's Parrot

Brett had a (parrot) named Nelly.
One day, Nelly was gone! Brett
forgot to close the cage. Brett
found Nelly nearby. Now Brett
always closes the cage. He knows
the cage keeps Nelly safe.

- -

Talk About It Complete the sentences.

Nelly is _____.
a parrot, safe in her cage

Brett _____.
had a parrot, always closes the cage

- -

Your Turn How is Brett being a good
animal owner? Tell a partner.

Retelling We use words to tell about something that happened in the past. Action words can help us tell about things that happened in the past.

The bird **ate** its food.

The bird **sat** in the cage.

Talk About It Circle the action words that tell about the past.

Todd walked his dog.

Gina fed her cat some food.

Sonya gave her bird some water.

Your Turn Retell the story of Brett and Nelly to a partner.

Plot and Theme **Plot** is what happens in a story. The plot can be about something that happened in the past. **Theme** is the main idea of a story.

Vanessa takes good care of her dog. Today, Vanessa walks her dog. Vanessa washes her dog. Then Vanessa dries her dog. After, she gives her dog food and water.

Talk About It Retell the plot of the story above. Tell a partner.

Your Turn Look back at the story on page 163. Which sentence below is the theme? Tell why you think so.

You should always keep a cage open.

A boy learns how to keep his pet safe.

Using *I* and *Me* We use *I* and *me* to talk about ourselves. *I* is always a capital letter. *I* usually comes before a verb. *Me* usually comes after a verb.

I fed the dog.

The dog ran to **me.**

· ·

Talk About It Circle *I* or *me* in each sentence.

I am a responsible animal owner.

My dog is happy to see me.

I like to pet my dog.

· ·

Your Turn Finish each sentence. Use *I* or *me.*

_____ have a pet cat.

My cat looks at _____.

Think, Talk, and Write

Taking Care of Pets Think about Brett and his parrot. People who have pets must be responsible. Tell a partner how to be a responsible pet owner.

food and water

safe place

Talk About It Review the vocabulary on page 162. Tell or show a partner what each word means.

Produce Language Write about how you would be a responsible animal owner. First draw a picture of you taking care of a pet. Complete the sentences. Then write in your Weekly Concept Journal.

I want a pet _____.

I would take care of my pet by _____.

Vocabulary

streets

trash

laugh

neighborhood

How can we be responsible friends and neighbors?

Friends are people we like. Neighbors are people who live near us. We should help our friends and neighbors. We should be nice to them.

Read the passage together.
Then circle the vocabulary words.

Helping Out

These people are cleaning up because they want their (neighborhood) to look nice. People clean up parks and streets. People pick up trash and throw it away. They laugh and have fun as they work.

Talk About It Complete the sentences.

Neighbors clean up their _____.
streets, neighborhood

Neighbors clean up by _____.
picking up trash

Your Turn Why should neighbors clean up their neighborhood? Tell a partner.

169

Explaining We use words to tell why something happens. The word *because* helps us explain, or tell why.

The park is clean **because** people pick up the trash.

These children are friends **because** they like each other.

. . . .

Talk About It Tell why you are a good neighbor.

I am a good neighbor because _____.

. . . .

Your Turn Why are you a good friend?

I am a good friend because _____.

Author's Purpose The **author's purpose** tells why an author writes something. Some authors want to explain something to us. The word *because* can help authors explain.

These people are responsible. They plant new trees because they want their neighborhood to look nice.

. . . .

Talk About It What is the author's purpose in the sentences above?

The author tells about _____.

. . . .

Your Turn Look at the story on page 169. What is the author's purpose?

The author tells about _____.

Different Kinds of Pronouns **Pronouns** can come before or after verbs. Some pronouns come before verbs. Other pronouns come after verbs.

Before Verbs	After Verbs
I, you, he, she, it, we, they	me, you, him, her, it, us, them

We threw away the trash.

Our neighbor thanked **us.**

Talk About It Complete each sentence with one of the pronouns.

Tina helped _____ clean up. (they, them)

_____ is a responsible friend. (She, Her)

Your Turn Write a sentence. Use a pronoun before or after a verb.

_____

_____

Think, Talk, and Write

Friends and Neighbors Cleaning up streets is one way to be a good neighbor. Tell a partner another way to be a responsible friend or neighbor.

friends

neighbors

Talk About It Review the vocabulary on page 168. Tell or show a partner what each word means.

Produce Language Write about how you are a responsible friend or neighbor. First draw a picture of you being a good friend or neighbor. Complete the sentences. Then write in your Weekly Concept Journal.

I am a responsible _____.

I am a good _____ because _____.

Vocabulary

talked

window

baseball
broke
mistake
truth

How can we be responsible when we make a mistake?

It is okay to make a mistake. But we should tell the truth about our mistake. We should try to fix our mistake too.

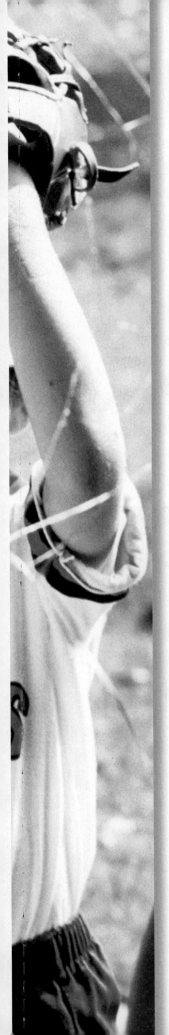

Read the passage together.
Then circle the vocabulary words.

The Mistake

Today I was playing baseball.
I broke my neighbor's window.
I talked to my neighbor about
my mistake. I said I want to pay
for a new window. My neighbor
thanked me for telling
the truth.

Talk About It Complete the sentences.

The boy _____.
broke a window, told the truth

The neighbor _____.
thanked the boy

Your Turn What did the boy do to
help after his mistake? Tell a partner.

Literary Analysis We use words to tell what a person wants to do.

Sharon **wants** to pay for the broken glass.

· ·

Talk About It Look at the picture. What does the boy want to do?

The boy wants to _____ .

· ·

Your Turn What is something you want to do? Tell a partner.

I want to _____ .

Author's Purpose

The **author's purpose** tells why an author writes something. Some authors want to tell about something.

Harry's puppy chewed up his homework. Harry is going to fix the puppy's mistake. He will do his homework again.

Talk About It How do you think Harry wants to be responsible? Why do you think the author wrote the story above? Tell a partner.

The author wants to _____.

Your Turn Look at the story "The Mistake" on page 175. Write how the author wants to fix his mistake.

The author wants to _____.

177

Contractions A **contraction** is a short way to say or write two words. It means the same thing as the two words. Contractions use a special mark to show where letters are left out.

Two Words	Contraction
are + not	aren't
is + not	isn't
do + not	don't
has + not	hasn't

I **do not** want to spill the milk.

I **don't** want to spill the milk.

. . . .

Talk About It Circle the contraction in each sentence.

Elena doesn't want to make a mistake.

The window wasn't broken.

I can't fix my mistake.

. . . .

Your Turn Circle the contraction that matches the underlined words.

She <u>is not</u> responsible. (don't, isn't)

They <u>are not</u> playing baseball. (aren't, hasn't)

Fixing Mistakes Think about how the boy who broke a window fixed his mistake. Tell a partner what you would do if you made a mistake.

tell the truth

fix it

· ·

Talk About It Review the vocabulary on page 174. Tell or show a partner what each word means.

· ·

Produce Language Write about how you fixed a mistake you made. First draw a picture of what happened. Complete the sentences. Then write in your Weekly Concept Journal.

I made a mistake when I _____.

I was responsible because _____.

Get Online!

Hear it!
See it!
Do it!

- Big Question Video
- Concept Talk Video
- Envision It! Animation
- Grammar Jammer
- Daily Journal

Traditions

THE BIG ?

Are traditions and celebrations important in our lives?

Sports
Why are sports traditions important in our country?

Flag Celebrations
What traditions and celebrations involve our country's flag?

Family Celebrations
Why are family celebrations special?

Cowboy Life
What can we learn about cowboy traditions?

Sharing Celebrations
How are traditions and celebrations shared?

Traditions

Vocabulary

PICTURE IT!

bat

PICTURE IT!

players

PICTURE IT!

wood

cheers
didn't
watched

Why are sports traditions important in our country?

Americans like to play and watch sports. One favorite sport is baseball. Families cheer their favorite players. They enjoy being together.

Read the passage together.
Then circle the vocabulary words.

A New Bat

In 1884, a boy watched a baseball game. Even then, people loved baseball. People yelled cheers. During the game, a baseball bat broke. Later, the boy made a new kind of bat. It was made out of a special kind of wood. Unlike the old bat, the bat didn't break. It was used by players everywhere.

· ·

Talk About It Complete the sentences below.

> At the baseball game _____.
> *a bat broke, people yelled cheers*
>
> The new bat _____.
> *was made of a special kind of wood,
> was used by players everywhere*

· ·

Your Turn Think about a sport you know.
Tell a partner about it.

Comparing We use words to tell how things are alike. We use the words *and, both,* and *like* to compare.

A baseball is round.   A basketball is round.

A baseball **and** a basketball are **both** round.
A baseball, **like** a basketball, is round.

Talk About It Compare the balls.

> Like a baseball, a
> soccer ball is _____ .

Your Turn Think of two other things used in sports. Compare them.

Both a _____ and a _____
are _____ .

Compare and Contrast What you read may tell how things are alike, or **compare** things. What you read may also tell how things are different, or **contrast** things. Clue words such as *like* compare. Words such as *different from* and *unlike* contrast.

Basketball   **Soccer Ball**   **Football**

A soccer ball is **like** a basketball. They are both round.

A football is **different from** a soccer ball. A football is oval.

Talk About It Read the sentences above. Tell a partner how the balls are alike and different.

Your Turn Read the passage on page 183. Contrast the old bat with the new bat.

The old bat was different from the new bat because _____.

Capital Letters We use **capital letters,** such as *A, B, C,* and *D,* when we write the names of days, months, and holidays. We also use capital letters in names and titles, such as *Dr., Ms.,* and *Mr.*

July

Sunday	Monday	Tuesday	Wednesday	Thursday	Friday	Saturday
1	2	3	4	5	6	7
8	9	10	11	12	13	14
15	16	17	18	19	20	21
22	23	24	25	26	27	28
29	30	31				

Talk About It Complete the sentences with a partner. Tell which words begin with capital letters.

Today is _____.

The month is _____.

Our sports coach is _____.

Your Turn Write three months of the year. Write an activity you like to do in each month.

_____

_____

_____

Think, Talk, and Write

Sports Think about how baseball is an American tradition. Tell a partner about other sports that we enjoy in our country.

basketball

football

Talk About It Review the vocabulary on page 182. Tell or show a partner what each word means.

Produce Language Write about a sport you like to play or watch. Tell why you like it. First draw a picture of the sport. Complete the sentences. Then write in your Weekly Concept Journal.

A sport I like is _____.

Players _____.

I like it because _____.

PICTURE IT!

flag

PICTURE IT!

stars

PICTURE IT!

stripes

celebration
freedom
tradition

What traditions and celebrations involve our country's flag?

The flag flies on Memorial Day and Labor Day. You see the flag at schools and at some homes. Where else can you find the flag?

Read the passage together.
Then circle the vocabulary words.

Our Flag

What do the (stars) and stripes
mean to people in the United
States? To many, the flag
means freedom. Others fly the
flag for tradition. Some fly it
to celebrate the birthday of
the United States.

Talk About It Complete the sentences below.

To some people, the flag means _____.
freedom, tradition

Some fly the flag to celebrate the
_____ of the United States.
birthday, tradition

Your Turn What does the flag mean
to you? Tell a partner.

189

Defining Special words help us tell about things in a group. Words, such as *holidays* and *celebrations,* can tell about a group of things. There are many kinds of holidays and celebrations.

Memorial Day is a **holiday.**   Fourth of July is a **holiday.**

· ·

Talk About It What word can you use to tell about Memorial Day and Fourth of July? Tell a partner.

Both are _____ .

· ·

Your Turn Look around your classroom. What are the names of some things you write with? Write a sentence.

_____

_____

Classify and Categorize When we read or look at pictures, we can put things that are alike into groups. The things below are all alike.

flagpole   telephone pole   ski poles

Talk About It Look at the pictures above. With a partner, name their group.

> They are all _____.

Your Turn Look at the pictures. Name their group.

     Both things are _____.

Quotation Marks A person's exact words are called a quotation. When we write a quotation, we use **quotation marks.** Quotation marks are placed at the beginning and at the end of the quotation.

Example: "Tonight, my family celebrates the Fourth of July," Jesal said.

Talk About It Read the sentences with a partner. Tell where quotation marks belong.

Would you like to join us? asked Jesal.

Sure I would, said Evan.

Your Turn Put quotation marks where they belong in the sentences below.

My mother said, Please hang the flag.

I will in a minute, I said.

Think, Talk, and Write

Flag Celebrations The U.S. flag is flown at celebrations and on holidays, such as Fourth of July. Tell a partner where and when you can see our country's flag.

at school

Fourth of July

- -

Talk About It Review the vocabulary on page 188. Tell or show a partner what each word means.

- -

Produce Language Write about a tradition or celebration when you see our country's flag. First draw a picture of the celebration or tradition. Complete the sentences. Then write in your Weekly Concept Journal.

I see the flag at _____.

The flag is used to celebrate _____.

Vocabulary

PICTURE IT!

basket

PICTURE IT!

candles

favorite
happiness

Why are family celebrations special?

Different families celebrate in different ways. Some families light candles and sing songs. Others tell stories or dance. No matter who you are, it's fun to celebrate!

Read the passage together.
Then circle the vocabulary words.

Celebrate Diwali!

Diwali is a celebration in India.
People light (candles) and lamps.
Families give a gift or basket
of fruit to their favorite
friends. Diwali is a time of
great joy and happiness.

- -

Talk About It Complete the sentences below.

Diwali is _____.
a celebration, a time of joy

During Diwali, it is a tradition to give
_____ of fruit to friends and family.
baskets, gifts

- -

Your Turn How do families celebrate
Diwali? Tell a partner.

Draw Conclusions We use words to tell what we think about things we see or read. We use *I think that* to say what we think.

I think that the girl in the picture is happy.

Talk About It What do you think is fun about Diwali? Tell a partner.

I think that _____.

Your Turn Look at the picture. Tell what you think.

_____

_____

Draw Conclusions We use what we read and what we know from real life to **draw conclusions.**

Thanksgiving is a celebration in the United States. Families eat a big meal. They also say thanks for all they have.

Talk About It Look at the photo. Read the passage. Draw a conclusion with a partner.

I think that Thanksgiving is _____.

Your Turn Reread the passage on page 195. Draw a conclusion about Diwali. Use *I think that* in your answer.

_____

_____

Using Commas We use **commas** in dates, locations, and addresses.

Dates	Locations
January 3, 2010	San Francisco, California
June 2, 2011	Haridwar, India
May 15, 2012	New York, NY 10010

April 10, 2010

Paula Escobar
124 Main Street
Sacramento, California

Dear Grandma,
   Thank you for inviting us over for Thanksgiving. I had such a fun time with you! I hope to see you soon!

Love,
Camila

Talk About It What is the date today? Tell a partner where the comma goes.

The date today is _____.

Your Turn Write your name and address. Don't forget the comma between the city and the state.

_____

_____

_____

Terence Winters
95 Walker Street
Los Angeles, California 90001

Think, Talk, and Write

Family Celebrations Think about how Indian families celebrate Diwali. Different families celebrate different traditions. Tell a partner about a special tradition that your family celebrates.

Kwanzaa

Thanksgiving

Talk About It Review the vocabulary on page 194. Tell or show a partner what each word means.

Produce Language Write about your favorite family tradition. Tell why it is special. First draw a picture of your family tradition. Complete the sentences. Then write in your Weekly Concept Journal.

My favorite family tradition is _____.

It is special because _____.

Vocabulary

PICTURE IT!

cattle

PICTURE IT!

cowboy

PICTURE IT!

herd

tireless

traveled

What can we learn about cowboy traditions?

Years ago, cowboys tended herds of cattle. Some cowboys traveled the country. They brought with them the songs and traditions of the West.

Read the passage together.
Then circle the vocabulary words.

Today's Cowboys

The job of a (cowboy) is to tend his herd of cattle. Cowboys ride horses. Today's tireless cowboys still sing and tell stories about life on the range.

Talk About It Complete the sentences below.

Cowboys _____.
ride horses, herd cattle

Cowboys _____ about life on the range.
sing, tell stories

Your Turn What do you know about cowboys? Tell a partner.

201

Cause-and-Effect Relationship We use words to tell why something happens. Special words, such as *because,* help us answer the question *why?*

The cowboys herded the cattle because they needed to get the cattle into the corral.

Circle the cause and effect word in the sentence above.

. . . .

Talk About It Look at the picture of the boy. Tell a partner why he is putting the saddle on the horse.

The boy puts the saddle on the horse because
_____ .

. . . .

Your Turn Why do you think cowboys tell stories and sing songs? Complete the sentence.

I think cowboys tell stories and sing songs because

_____ .

Cause and Effect We may read about something that happens. This is called an **effect.** We may also read about why something happens. This is called a **cause.** The clue word *because* shows cause and effect.

The cowboy was tired because he had worked all day. He decided to take a rest. He fell asleep. After a while, he woke up. He felt better because he took a nap.

Circle the clue words in the paragraph above.

. . . .

Talk About It What caused the cowboy to be tired? Tell a partner the cause and effect.

> The cause is _____.
>
> The effect is that the cowboy was tired.

. . . .

Your Turn Look at the paragraph again. What caused the cowboy to feel better? Write a sentence.

_____

_____

Compound Sentences A **compound sentence** contains two sentences that are joined by a comma and a connecting word. Connecting words are *and, or, but, yet, so,* and *nor.*

In a compound sentence, a comma comes before the connecting word.

> I want to read a cowboy story, **but** first I must clean my room.

Talk About It Tell a partner where the comma belongs in each sentence.

> I want to write about cowboys and I want to draw my own pictures.
>
> My story will be long so I will need many pictures.

Your Turn Use the connecting word *and* to connect these two sentences. Don't forget the comma.

The grass was high. The sun was hot.

_____

_____

Think, Talk, and Write

Cowboy Life Think about what a cowboy's life is like. Tell a partner about some cowboy traditions.

herding

telling stories

Talk About It Review the vocabulary on page 200. Tell or show a partner what each word means.

Produce Language Write about cowboy traditions. First draw a picture of one cowboy tradition. Complete the sentences. Then write in your Weekly Concept Journal.

Cowboys ride _____ and herd _____ .

Cowboys also _____ .

Vocabulary

PICTURE IT!

dumplings

PICTURE IT!

festival

PICTURE IT!

meal

**dragon
guests
midway**

How are traditions and celebrations shared?

People celebrate together in many ways. Sometimes people cook and enjoy a meal together. They might also enjoy festivals outside with other people.

Read the passage together.
Then circle the vocabulary words.

Dragon Boat Festival

The (Dragon) Boat Festival is held midway through each year in China. To celebrate, people ride in colorful boats that are shaped like dragons. They race each other across the water.

People also prepare special foods to celebrate this festival. They have fun preparing dumplings for their guests and eating together. The festival is fun for everyone.

. . . .

Talk About It Complete the sentences below.

At the Dragon Boat Festival, people _____.
race boats, make special foods

The Dragon Boat Festival is _____.
held midway through each year,
fun for everyone

. . . .

Your Turn How do Chinese people prepare for the Dragon Boat Festival? Tell a partner.

Draw Conclusions We use special words to tell what we think about things. We use the words *I think that* to tell what we think. We use *because* to tell why we think something.

I think that preparing special foods takes a lot of work **because** these people look very busy!

Talk About It Use special words to tell how you feel about preparing a special meal.

> I think that preparing a special meal
> is _____ because _____.

Your Turn Write a sentence that uses the words *I think that* to tell what you think about the Dragon Boat Festival. Use *because* to tell why you think that.

_____

_____

Draw Conclusions We use what we know and what we read or see to **draw conclusions.** When we draw conclusions, we get new ideas about a story. We use the words *I think that* to tell a conclusion. We use *because* to explain a conclusion.

Read the paragraph.

Katie helps her family make food for Sunday dinner. They bake potatoes. They grill fish. They cook vegetables. For Sunday dinner, the whole family is together.

Talk About It Draw a conclusion about how the family feels about Sunday dinner.

I think that the family _____ because _____.

Your Turn Look at the passage on page 207. Draw a conclusion about why you think that the festival is fun for everyone.

_____

_____

Paragraphs A **paragraph** is a group of sentences that tell about a single topic. We indent, or add spaces, to show where a new paragraph begins.

    We are having a celebration on Saturday. My family and I have been preparing all week. It has been a lot of fun.

    Today, we made some bread for the celebration. It is difficult to make bread!

. . . .

Talk About It Read the paragraphs above. Say "new paragraph" when you get to the beginning of a paragraph.

. . . .

Your Turn How can you tell where a new paragraph begins? Explain here.

_____

_____

_____

Think, Talk, and Write

Sharing Celebrations Think about how people in China celebrate the Dragon Boat Festival. Tell a partner how people celebrate traditions together.

cooking

gathering

Talk About It Review the vocabulary on page 206. Tell or show a partner what each word means.

Produce Language Write about how people celebrate traditions together. First draw a picture of what people do to prepare for the celebration. Then tell what happens during the celebration. Complete the sentences. Then write in your Weekly Concept Journal.

People _____ to prepare for a celebration.

During a celebration, guests _____.

Glossary

How to Use This Glossary

This glossary can help you understand and pronounce some of the words in this book. The words at the top of each page show the first and last words on the page. The pronunciation key is on page 213. Remember, if you can't find the word you are looking for, ask for help or check a dictionary.

The entry word is in dark type. It shows how the word is spelled.

The pronunciation is in parentheses. It also shows which syllables are stressed.

Part-of-speech labels show the function of the word.

adapt (ə dapt′), *v.* to change your behavior or ideas to fit a new situation

Aa

ambulance (am′byə ləns), *N.* a special vehicle for carrying people who are sick or injured

artist (är′tist), *N.* someone who paints or draws pictures or does something else creative

astronauts (as′trə nòts), *N.* people who travel into space

attend (ə tend′), *v.* to go to or be at an event or class

autumn (ò′təm), *N.* the season between summer and winter, when the leaves fall off the trees

Bb

badger (baj′ər), *N.* a wild animal with black and white fur that lives in a hole

bags (bagz), *N.* containers made of cloth, paper, plastic, or leather, used for carrying things

band (band), *N.* a group of people who play music together

baseball (bās′bòl′), *N.* a game that is played on a special field with a ball and with a long stick

basket (bas′kit), *N.* a container made of thin pieces of wood or dried plants used for carrying things

bat (bat), *N.* a long piece of wood used for hitting the ball in baseball

bear (bâr), *N.* a large, wild animal with thick fur

birds (bėrdz), *N.* animals with wings and feathers that lay eggs and usually can fly

blossoms (blos′əmz), *N.* new flowers on a tree or bush

boxes (boks′iz), *N.* containers with four straight sides, usually made of hard paper or wood

branches (branch′iz), N. parts of a tree that grow out from it

broke (brōk), V. came apart or was hurt

buckets (buk′its), N. big containers that can hold water

bundle (bun′dl), N. a group of things such as papers or clothes that are tied together

burrow (bėr′ō), N. a hole in the ground made by a small animal

burrs (bėrz), N. the prickly coverings of some fruits and seeds that cling to things

busy (biz′ē), ADJ. full of many people or things

butterflies (but′ər flīz′), N. insects that have large wings with bright colors

Cc

cage (kāj), N. a box made of metal wires in which you keep birds or animals

candles (kan′dlz), N. pieces of wax with strings in the middle that you burn to give light

cattle (kat′l), N. large animals kept for their meat, milk, and skins

celebration (sel′ə brā′shən), N. a special meal or party that you have because something good has happened

cheers (chirz), N. shouts of happiness or support

city (sit′ē), N. a very large town

claws (klȯz), N. the hard sharp parts on the foot of an animal

climb (klim), V. to go up something

clothes (klōz), N. things that you wear on your body

communicate (kə myü′nə kāt), V. to speak or write to someone

community (kə myü′nə tē), N. all the people living in one place

couldn't (ku̇d′nt), COULD NOT

country (kun′trē), N. the land that is outside a city or town

cowboy (kou′boi′), N. a man who rides a horse and takes care of cattle

creative (krē ā′tiv), ADJ. good at making new and interesting things

crops (krops), N. plants that a farmer grows

Dd

damage (dam′ij), N. harm that has been done to something

dangerous (dān′jər əs), ADJ. able or likely to harm you

didn't (did′nt), DID NOT

different (dif′ər ənt), ADJ. not the same

difficult (dif′ə kult), ADJ. not easy to do or understand

door (dôr), N. the flat piece of wood or metal that you push or pull to go into a room

dragon (drag′ən), N. a fierce animal in stories that has wings and can breathe out fire

dumplings (dump′lingz), N. pieces of dough, sometimes filled, that are cooked in liquid

a in hat	ėr in term	ô in order	ch in child	ə = a in about
ā in age	i in it	oi in oil	ng in long	ə = e in taken
â in care	ī in ice	ou in out	sh in she	ə = i in pencil
ä in far	o in hot	u in cup	th in thin	ə = o in lemon
e in let	ō in open	u̇ in put	ᴛʜ in then	ə = u in circus
ē in equal	ȯ in all	ü in rule	zh in measure	

Glossary

213

Ee

easier (ē′zē ər), *ADJ.* less difficult; done with no trouble

enjoy (en joi′), *v.* to get pleasure and happiness from something

enough (i nuf′), *ADJ.* as much as needed

explained (ek splānd′), *v.* made something easy to understand

Ff

fair (fâr), *ADJ.* equal for everyone

family (fam′ə lē), *N.* a group of people who are related to each other, such as moms and dads and children

far away (fär ə wā), *ADV.* not close by

favorite (fā′vər it), *N.* someone or something that you like more than any other

festival (fes′tə vəl), *N.* a set of special events

fire truck (fir truk), *N.* a large vehicle with hoses and water that helps firefighters stop fires

firefighter (fir′fi′tər), *N.* a person whose job is to stop fires

first aid kit (fėrst′ād kit), *N.* a box that holds medicine and bandages to help someone who is sick or hurt

flag (flag), *N.* a piece of cloth with a special pattern on it, used as the symbol of a country

forgot (fər got′), *v.* was unable to think of or remember

freedom (frē′dəm), *N.* the state of being able to do what you want

friends (frendz), *N.* people who you like very much

Gg

great (grāt), *ADJ.* very good

guests (gests), *N.* people who are visiting someone else's house

Hh

happiness (hap′ē nis), *N.* the state of being pleased

harvest (här′vist), *v.* to gather crops from the fields

heavy (hev′ē), *ADJ.* weighing a lot

herd (hėrd), *N.* a group of animals of the same kind

hiking (hīk′ing), *v.* taking a long walk in the country or in the mountains

hours (ourz), *N.* amounts of time, each equal to 60 minutes

hurricane (hər′ə kān), *N.* a dangerous storm with very strong, fast winds

Ii

imagine (i ma′jən), *v.* to form pictures and ideas in your mind

instead (in sted′), *ADV.* in place of

instruments (in′strə məntz), *N.* things used to make music

invent (in vent′), *v.* to think of an idea, or to make something for the first time

Kk

knows (nōz), *v.* has information or facts about something

Ll

laugh (laf), *v.* to make a sound that shows that you are happy or think something is funny

learn (lėrn), *v.* to get information or facts about something

listen (lis′n), *v.* to pay attention to what someone is saying or to something that you hear

Mm

many (men′ē), *ADJ.* a lot; a large number of

meal (mēl), *N.* the food that you eat at one time

members (mem′bərz), *N.* people who have joined a group or organization

midway (mid′wā′), *ADV.* in the middle of

minute (min′it), *N.* an amount of time equal to 60 seconds

mistake (mə stā′kən), *N.* something that is not correct

monkey (mung′kē), *N.* a small, furry animal that has a long tail and climbs trees

mother (muᴛʜ′ər), *N.* a female parent

move (müv), *V.* to go to a new place to live or work

much (much), *ADJ.* a lot; a large amount of

Nn

neighborhood (nā′bər hùd), *N.* a small area of a town and the people who live there

Oo

operator (op′ə rā′tər), *N.* someone who controls the telephone calls made to or from a place

outside (out′sīd′), *ADV.* outdoors in nature

owners (ō′nərz), *N.* people who have something that belongs to them

Pp

paint (pānt), *V.* to put a colored liquid on a surface

parrot (par′ət), *N.* a brightly-colored tropical bird often kept as a pet

people (pē′pəl), *N.* more than one person

picnic (pik′nik), *N.* a time when you take food and eat it outdoors

planning (plan′ing), *V.* thinking about how to do something

players (plā′ərz), *N.* people who play a game or a sport

pretty (prit′ē), *ADJ.* nice to look at

probably (prob′ə blē), *ADV.* likely to happen or to be true

Qq

quickly (kwik′lē), *ADV.* done or happening in a short time

quilt (kwilt), *N.* a soft, thick cover for a bed

Rr

rebuild (rē bild′), *V.* to repair or make like new again

repack (rē pak′), *V.* to pack again

responsible (ri spon′sə bəl), *ADJ.* taking care of someone or something

river (riv′ər), *N.* a long body of water that goes into an ocean or a lake

Ss

safe (sāf), *ADJ.* not in danger of being harmed

sculpture (skulp′chər), *N.* an object made from wood, stone, or metal

seed (sēd), *N.* a small grain from which a new plant grows

show (shō), *V.* to let someone see something

shuttle (shut′l), *N.* a vehicle that can fly into space and return to Earth

soil (soil), *N.* the earth in which plants grow

solve (solv), *V.* to find the answer to something

soon (sün), *ADV.* in a short time from now

space (spās), *N.* the area away from the Earth, where the sun and stars are

stars (stärz), *N.* shapes with five or six points

stone (stōn), *N.* a smooth piece of rock

straight (strāt), *ADJ.* not bending or curved

strange (strānj), *ADJ.* unusual, surprising, or difficult to understand

streets (strēts), *N.* roads in a town or city where cars are driven

stripes (strīps), *N.* long thin lines of color

suitcases (süt′kās′ez), *N.* large bags used to carry clothes

sunrise (sun′rīz′), *N.* the time in the morning when the sun first comes up

surprised (sər prīzd′), *V.* saw something that was new or not expected

Tt

table (tā′bəl), *N.* a piece of flat wood or metal with four legs

take care (tāk kâr), *V.* to give another person or animal things they need

talked (tȯkd), *V.* said things to someone; spoke

teach (tēch), *V.* to give lessons about any subject

tiger (tī′gər), *N.* a large, strong wildcat that has yellow fur with black lines

tireless (tīr′lis), *ADJ.* not ever getting tired; always having energy

today (tə dā′), *ADV.* the day it is now

tools (tülz), *N.* things that help you build or repair

touch fastener (tuch fas′n ər), *N.* two pieces of fabric that stick together, used often for shoes or clothes

town (toun), *N.* a place with many houses and stores where people live and work

tradition (trə dish′ən), *N.* a belief or custom that has existed for a long time

trash (trash), *N.* waste material such as old food and dirty paper

traveled (trav′əld), *V.* having made a trip from one place to another

truth (trüth), *N.* the correct or true facts

tunnels (tun′lz), *N.* passages under the ground

Uu

underground (un′dər ground′), *ADJ.* under the ground; under the earth's surface

unhappy (un hap′ē), *ADJ.* sad or worried; not happy

unpack (un pak′), *V.* to take things out of a box or bag

Vv

village (vil′ij), *N.* a very small town

Ww

warm (wôrm), *ADJ.* slightly hot, but not too hot

watched (wächd), *V.* looked at something and paid attention to it

water (wȯ′tər), *N.* the clear liquid in rain, rivers, and lakes

water lilies (wȯ′tər lil′ēz), *N.* plants with leaves and flowers that live in water

weather (weᴛн′ər), *N.* the temperature and the wind, rain, or sun

whatever (wät ev′ər), *PRONOUN.* any or all of the things that are needed or wanted

wheels (wēlz), *N.* the round things under something that turn around and around and allow it to move

whole (hōl), *ADJ.* complete

window (win′dō), *N.* an opening with glass across it in a wall of a building

wood (wŭd), *N.* the material of which the trunks and branches of trees are made

work (wėrk), *V.* to do a job

world (wėrld), *N.* Earth and all the people and things in it

worst (wėrst), *ADJ.* worse than anything else

wrapped (rapd), *ADJ.* covered by something such as paper or cloth

Credits

Illustrations

35-37 Reed Sprunger; 132-133 William Melvin; 165 Rick Drennan; 172 Doron Ben-Ami

Photographs

Every effort has been made to secure permission and provide appropriate credit for photographic material. The publisher deeply regrets any omission and pledges to correct errors called to its attention in subsequent editions.

Unless otherwise acknowledged, all photographs are the property of Pearson Education, Inc.

Photo locators denoted as follows: Top (T), Center (C), Bottom (B), Left (L), Right (R), Background (Bkgd)

20 ©Michael & Patricia Fogden/Corbis; 22 (TL) ©Alan Spencer/Powered by Light/Alamy Images, (TL) Jupiter Images, (CL) ©Ed Freeman/The Image Bank/Getty Images, (BL) ©Sonya Farrell/The Image Bank/Getty Images, (C) ©Jose Fuste Raga/Corbis; 23 (TL) ©Museum of Flight/Corbis, (TL) ©John Crum/Alamy Images, (TR) ©Emmerich-Webb/Photonica/Getty Images; 24 (TL) ©Jupiter Images/Brand X/Alamy, (TC) ©Robert Glenn/DK Stock/Getty Images, (TR) ©Jutta Klee/Corbis; 25 ©Peter Cade/Riser/Getty Images; 26 (BR) ©Jupiter Images/BananaStock/Alamy, (TR) ©Jupiter Images/Brand X/Alamy, (C) ©Alan Thornton/Taxi/Getty Images; 27 (CR) ©Corbis Premium RF/Alamy, (TR) Fotolia; 28 (CL) NASA, (BL) Anglo-Australian Observatory/©DK Images, (TL) Corbis, (C) ©NASA/Science Source/Photo Researchers, Inc.; 29 ©NASA/Getty Images; 30 (BR) Getty Images, (CR) ©Stuart O'Sullivan/Stone/Getty Images; 31 NASA; 32 (TR) Jupiter Images, (BR) ©AFP/AFP/Getty Images; 33 (CR) NASA, (TR) ©Royal Observatory Edinburgh/SPL/Photo Researchers, Inc.; 34 (BL) ©Blend Images/Alamy, (TL) ©DK Images, (CL) ©Roy Ooms/All Canada Photos/Getty Images, (C) ©Reg Charity/Corbis; 35 ©Norbert Rosing/National Geographic Image Collection; 36 (TR) ©Johner Images/Getty Images, (CR) ©J. M. Foujols/Stock Image/Jupiter Images; 38 (CR) ©Jupiter Images/BananaStock/Alamy, (BR) ©Purestock/Alamy, (TR) ©Tom Walker/Photographer's Choice/Getty Images; 39 (CR) ©Phyllis Greenberg/Animals Animals/Earth Scenes, (TR) ©Tom Brakefield/Corbis; 40 (BL) Getty Images, (TL) ©Purestock/Alamy, (C) ©Pierre Jacques/hemis.fr/Getty Images, (CL) ©Anthony West/Corbis; 41 ©Jupiter Images/Comstock Images/Alamy; 42 (CL) Getty Images, (TR) ©Image Source, (BR) ©Ross Whitaker/The Image Bank/Getty Images; 44 (CR) Getty Images, (TR) ©National Geographic/Getty Images; 45 (CR, TR) ©Corbis/Jupiter Images; 46 (BL) Jerry Young/©DK Images, (TL) Getty Images, (CL) ©Gary Vestal/Photographer's Choice/Getty Images, (C) Getty Images; 47 ©Gail Shumway/Photographer's Choice RR/Getty Images; 48 (CR) Fuse/Getty Images (TL) Geoff Brightling/©DK Images, (TR) ©DK Images, (TC) ©Frans Lemmens/The Image Bank/Getty Images, (CL) ©Steve Byland/Fotolia, (BR) Thinkstock; 49 (TC) ©DK Images, (BR) ©Rubberball/Getty Images, (TR) Thinkstock, (TL) ©Thom Lang/Corbis; 50 (BR) Andy Crawford/©DK Images, (TR) ©Timothy Laman/National Geographic/Getty Images; 51 (TR) ©J. Marshall/Alamy Images, (CR) ©Stuart Westmorland/Corbis; 52 ©Bernard Annebicque/Sygma/Corbis; 54 (TL) ©AFP/Getty Images, (TL) ©James Leynse/Corbis, (TL) ©Michael Pole/Corbis, (TL) ©Design Pics Inc./Alamy, (TL, C) Getty Images, (CL) ©Bob Peterson/Getty Images; 55 Jupiter Images; 56 (TL) ©Sascha Pflaeging/Getty Images, (TC) ©Corey Hochachka/Design Pics/Corbis, (TR) ©Vince Streano/Getty Images; 57 (BL) ©David J. Turner/Getty Images, (BC, BR) Getty Images; 58 (TL) ©ML Harris/Getty Images, (TR) Getty Images, (TC) ©Visions of America, LLC/Alamy; 59 (TR) ©Peter Samuels/Getty Images, (CR) ©Uppercut Images/Alamy; 60 (TL) ©Mark Lewis/Getty Images, (CL) Getty Images, (C) ©Bill Haber/AP Images; 61 ©Mario Tama/Staff/Getty Images; 62 (TC) ©Marie Dubrac/Corbis, (TR) ©Chris Dyball/Innerlight/Getty Images, (BR) ©Jim West/PhotoEdit; 63 ©Walter Rawlings/Getty Images; 64 (TR) ©Erik Von Weber/Getty Images, (CL) ©White Packert/Getty Images, (C) ©Richard H Johnston/Getty Images, (CR) ©Bryan Peterson/Corbis; 65 (CR) ©Jim West/PhotoEdit, (TR) ©Kayte M. Deioma/PhotoEdit; 66 (TL) ©Jan Butchofsky-Houser/Corbis, (CL) ©Moodboard/Corbis, (C) Getty Images; 67 (TR) Andy Crawford/©DK Images, (CR) Dave King/©DK Images; 68 (TL) ©Niclas Albinsson/Jupiter Images, (TC) ©Mark Bolton/Corbis, (TR) ©Corbis Premium RF/Alamy; 69 (CR) ©zefa/Corbis/Jupiter Images, (CL) Rojo Images/Fotolia; 70 (TL) ©Asia Images Group/Alamy, (TR) ©Valuline/Punchstock, (CL) ©Fancy Photography/Veer, Inc., (BR) ©Ulrich Kerth/Getty Images, (CR) ©Fancy Photography/Veer, Inc.; 71 (TR) ©Blend Images/Alamy, (CR) ©Kayte M. Deioma/PhotoEdit; 72 (TL) ©David Stluka/Getty Images, (CL) ©Richard Price/Getty Images, (BL) ©Donald Miralle/Getty Images, (C) ©Ted Streshinsky/Corbis; 73 ©Spencer Grant/PhotoEdit; 74 (CR) ©Michael Newman/PhotoEdit, (BR) ©Myrleen Ferguson Cate/PhotoEdit; 75 ©Dirk Anschutz/Getty Images; 76 (CL) ©Jim Vecchi/Corbis, (CR) ©Benjamin Rondel/Corbis, (TR) ©Bob Krist/Corbis, (TL) ©Image Source; 77 (TR) ©Scott Indermaur/Jupiter Image, (CR) ©Lori Adamski Peek/Getty Images; 78 (TL) ©Jupiter Images/Brand X/Alamy, (CL) Stockdisc, (C) Getty Images; 79 (CR) Getty Images, (TR) ©DK Images; 80 (TL) ©Design Pics Inc./Alamy, (TR) ©Corbis Super RF/Alamy, (BL) ©South West Images Scotland/Alamy Images, (BR) ©Image Source; 81 (TR) ©AGB Photo/Alamy, (BR) ©Lew Long/Corbis, (CR) ©Tom & Dee Ann McCarthy/Corbis; 82 (TR) ©D. Hurst/Alamy, (BR) ©Superstudio/Getty Images; 83 (CR) ©Lauren Burke/Getty Images, (TR) ©S. Kuttig/plainpicture/Corbis; 84 ©Mike Timo/Getty Images; 86 ©Mike Timo/Getty Images, (TL) ©Kitt Cooper-Smith/Alamy Images, (TL) ©Masterfile Royalty-Free, (TL) ©Jim Cummins/Corbis, (TL) ©George Disario/Corbis, (TL) ©Olle Lindstedt/Getty Images, (CL) ©Peter Hendrie/Getty Images, (C) ©Nik Wheeler/Alamy Images; 87 Getty Images; 88 (TL) ©Altrendo Images/Getty Images, (TR) ©Sante Milio/Getty Images; 89 (TL) ©Peter Hendrie/Getty Images, (TR) ©Altrendo travel/Getty Images; 90 (CR) ©Jim Sugar/Corbis, (TR) ©Jupiter Images/Pixland/Alamy; 91 ©Robert Harding Picture Library Ltd/Alamy Images; 92 (CL) ©Pat Crowe II/Getty Images, (BL) ©Altrendo Nature/Getty Images, (C) ©Archive Iconografico/Corbis, (TL) ©Corbis/Jupiter Images; 93 Jupiter Images; 94 (TL) SuperStock, (TR, BR) ©The Art Archive/Corbis, (CR) ©Peter Willi/SuperStock; 95 (TR) ©The Gallery Collection/Corbis, (BR) ©The Bridgeman Art Library/Getty Images; 96 (TR) ©Randy Faris/Corbis, (BR) ©Diana Koenigsberg/Jupiter Images; 97 (TR) ©LHB Photo/Alamy, (CR) ©Robbie Jack/Corbis; 98 (CL) ©Elisa Cicinelli/Jupiter Images, (C) ©Ulrich Baumgarten/vario images/Alamy Images,

WORDS!

A Vocabulary Handbook

Antonyms

Antonyms are words that have opposite meaning. *Messy* and *neat* are antonyms.

Synonyms

Synonyms are words that have the same meaning or similar meaning. *Happy* and *glad* are synonyms.

Happy

Glad

Knowing and using synonyms can help make your writing more interesting. Look in a thesaurus to find synonyms.

Base Words

A base word is a word that cannot be broken
down into smaller words or word parts.
Appear and *cloud* are base words.

Appear

Knowing the meaning of a
base word can help you
understand the meaning of
longer words.

Cloud

Prefixes

A prefix is a word part that can be added to the beginning of a base word. In the word *disappear, dis-* is a prefix.

Appear	Disappear

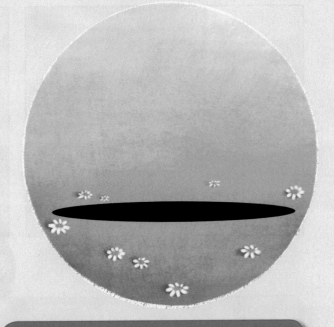

Knowing the meaning of a prefix can help you figure out the meaning of the new word.

Common Prefixes and Their Meanings

un-	not
re-	again, back
in-	not
dis-	not, opposite of
pre-	before

Suffixes

A suffix is a word part added to the end of a base word. In the word *cloudless*, *-less* is a suffix.

Cloud

Cloudless

Common Suffixes and Their Meanings

-able	can be done
-ment	action or process
-less	without
-tion	act, process

Knowing how a suffix changes a word can help you figure out the meaning of the new word.

Context Clues

Read the words before and after a word that you don't know to help you make sense of it.

I saw a robin, a bluebird, a sapsucker, and a turkey while walking in the woods.

Word Families

Word families are related words that have the same base word. *Bicycle*, *recycle*, and *cyclone* belong to the same word family. They all have the base word *cycle*.

Bicycle

Cyclone

Recycle

If you know what the base word means, you may be able to figure out the meaning of words related to it.

Compound Words

Compound words are words made of two smaller words. *Goldfish* and *basketball* are compound words.

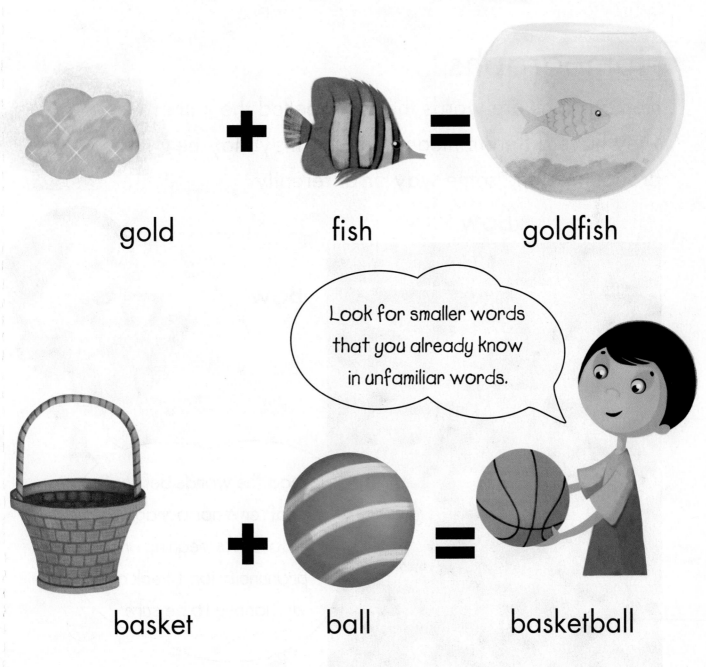

gold + fish = goldfish

Look for smaller words that you already know in unfamiliar words.

basket + ball = basketball

Multiple-Meaning Words

Multiple-meaning words are words that can have different meanings depending on how they are used.

Homographs

Homographs are words that are spelled the same. They have different meanings, and they may be pronounced the same way or differently.

Bow

Bow

Read the words before and after a homograph to discover its meaning and pronunciation. Check a dictionary to be sure.

Homonyms

Homonyms are words that are spelled the same. They have different meanings, and they are pronounced the same way.

Pen

Pen

You can figure out the meaning of a homonym by reading the words around it.

Homophones

Homophones are words that sound the same, but they are spelled differently and they have different meanings.

Night

Knight

Homophones might be confusing when *you* hear them being read aloud. Pay attention to the words before and after the homophone to find its meaning.

Dictionary

A dictionary is a book that explains the words of our language. The words in a dictionary are in alphabetical order.

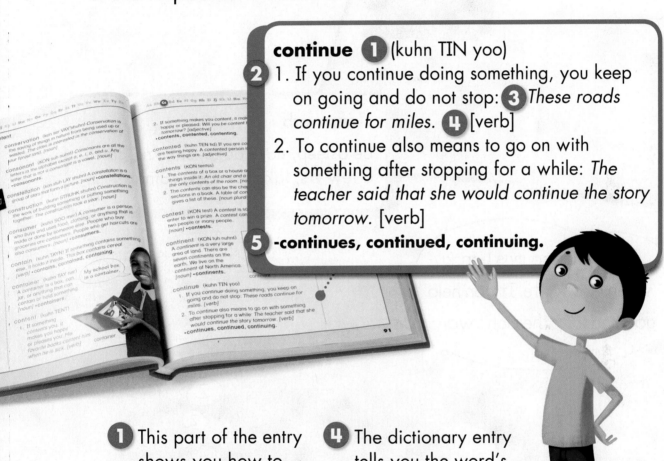

continue ❶ (kuhn TIN yoo)
❷ 1. If you continue doing something, you keep on going and do not stop: ❸ *These roads continue for miles.* ❹ [verb]
2. To continue also means to go on with something after stopping for a while: *The teacher said that she would continue the story tomorrow.* [verb]
❺ -continues, continued, continuing.

❶ This part of the entry shows you how to pronounce the word.

❷ Here is the word's definition.

❸ The word is used in an example to help you understand its meaning.

❹ The dictionary entry tells you the word's part of speech. *Continue* is a verb.

❺ See how the word changes when it has a suffix added.

Thesaurus

A thesaurus is a book of synonyms. The words in a thesaurus are in alphabetical order.

sleep verb

be asleep, nap, doze, snooze, catch a few z's, take a siesta, catnap

Keep a thesaurus handy when you write. It can help you find just the right word.